HUMAN HORIZONS SERIES

EASY TO MAKE AIDS FOR ELDERLY PEOPLE

Don Caston
with drawings by Joan Thompson

A CONDOR BOOK
SOUVENIR PRESS (E&A) LTD

To Senor Francisco Palmer y Senora Amparo Benito,
y
Senor José Martin Gonzales y Senora Andrea Gail Santos
y Hij Calixto Martin Gail y Yolanda Martin Gail who have
have made me so welcome in their Spain

ISBN 0 285 65004 1 Casebound
ISBN 0285 65005 X Paperback

Filmset and printed in Great Britain by
BAS Printers Limited, Over Wallop, Hampshire

CONTENTS

Outside the House and in the Garden

INTRODUCTION

As I grow older I am beginning to feel the need for a 'little-something-or-other' to help me do a number of jobs that not so long ago I did without thinking. Perhaps anatomically I am changing, with my arms getting shorter and my legs longer, because I now seem to have a problem reaching down to put on my shoes, and an even greater one when I want to take them off. I am also beginning to find that things about my home are changing; for instance, shelves are getting higher, the bottom drawer of the chest of drawers in my bedroom is now much lower than it used to be, and it has also become much heavier and more difficult to open and close. The more I think about it, there does not seem to be one room that has not changed in some way or other. Out in the garden it's the same story—all the tools are heavier and definitely harder to use, and when it comes to weeding, the weeds now grow at an alarming rate with roots intent on going down to Australia.

The last thing I want is to be surrounded by gadgets, but if they allow me to keep my independence I shall accept them as part of growing older. You will note that I did not use the word old because that is something I shall never accept.

I think the same thoughts will go through my mind if one day it is suggested that I should have a wheelchair or some other hospital-type pieces of furniture in the home. Before I accept these chrome-plated and plastic things I shall want to know if my favourite armchair, dining room chair, or whatever it is they suggest should be changed, cannot be safely modified so that I can continue to live with all the goods and chattels which have been part of my life for so long. There is no way that my home is going to even start looking like a hospital ward.

It was with all this in mind that I was prompted to write this book. I hope to show that it is possible to have a little help around the home which will not advertise the fact that you are getting older, or that you are a handicapped person.

It is not suggested that you yourself should make all the things your medical adviser considers would help you, but there is no reason why you should not lend a hand when family and friends are making them for you. Alternatively, having taught in schools, I know that there are many teachers of technical studies who are looking for projects like these which involve a little design, making something useful and, possibly even more important, working with the community; they may be willing to get their pupils to make small items for you.

Some of the aids are, of course, available through the DHSS and suppliers of appliances, but the advantage of having them made for you is that, with the help of your medical adviser, they will be tailored to your own exact requirements—there will be no need to push cushions or pillows between you and the chair to make you comfortable, the foot rest will be at exactly the right height and lights will be in the best places for you personally.

It is very important that you seek the advice of your doctor or health visitor before making or having made any of the aids suggested in this book. They will be very pleased to help you and will very often make some good suggestions from a medical point of view. They will also be able to teach you how to use the aids.

SYMBOLS USED IN THE BOOK

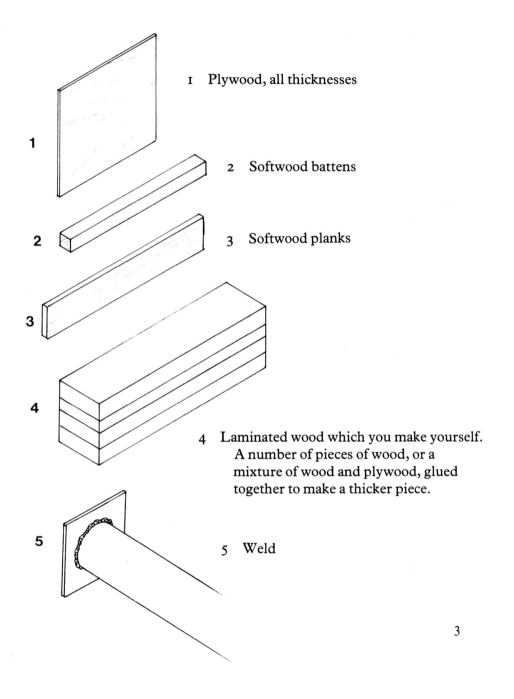

1   Plywood, all thicknesses

2   Softwood battens

3   Softwood planks

4   Laminated wood which you make yourself.
A number of pieces of wood, or a
mixture of wood and plywood, glued
together to make a thicker piece.

5   Weld

GLOSSARY OF CONSTRUCTION TERMS

Fix: Throughout this book 'fix' means to join together by glue and nails, glue and screws, nuts and bolts or self-tapping screws. In the case of dowelling, it means to glue into a drilled hole.

Cut Out: Cut out means sawing wood with any kind of saw.

Pilot Holes: These are holes drilled through the wood before driving home a nail or screw, to minimise the risk of splitting it. The diameter of the hole is usually about half that of the nail or screw.

Drive Fit: A drive fit is when a dowel has to be knocked into the hole with a hammer. A little glue is put in the hole first. Care must be taken not to split the wood.

Marking Out: This means drawing lines and making marks on the wood with a pencil to indicate where to saw, drill a hole or shape it in some way. If a line is drawn in the wrong place, draw a wavy line through it, because it is all too easy to saw down the wrong line. When all the marking out has been completed, spend a few moments checking the lines to make sure that they are dimensionally in the right place.

Laminating: It is not always possible to buy a short length of wood or a piece of plywood in the width or thickness required for a particular job. This problem can often be overcome by glueing pieces of wood together as illustrated. Apply the glue evenly but not thickly and keep the wood under pressure while the glue dries.

5

SAFETY

A habit must be formed of regularly checking the home and listing all the items which are starting to need attention. **Don't wait until there is an accident.**

As soon as a light starts to flicker when the switch is touched, a wire lead starts to fray, or there is the slightest smell of gas, a loose screw, a water leak—whatever it is, get it seen to **at once.**

Home and furniture modifications must also be examined carefully and regularly; not only for the workmanship, but you may have changed a little, making another alteration necessary. Never put your independence at stake.

Get all the booklets you can on home safety.

BUYING THE WOOD

To make modifications to some furniture less noticeable, the wood may have to be stained instead of painted. To get a truer match, it is often better to use second-hand wood of the same type. This can be obtained by buying a piece of old furniture and carefully taking it apart. Make sure the wood is sound and completely free from wood worm before purchase.

For any other wood required, it is best to go to the local DIY shop. Here will be found a good selection of both solid timber and plywood. The cheapest way to buy wood is from those shops which sell off-cuts. With a flexible rule, measure each piece you pick out to make sure it is large enough and of the right thickness. Always check for faults such as end splits, knots, twisting and bowing, and de-laminating of the layers of the plywood.

Also make sure that any plywood or blockboard is not too flexible. A larger piece usually bends more easily in one direction than the other, so if a strip of plywood, cut lengthwise, for instance, is not stiff enough, try to find a piece that has been cut crosswise or from another part of the sheet.

Throughout this book the thickness of plywood is given only in metric sizes, as this is the way it is usually sold.

TOOL KIT

It is not necessary to go out and spend a small fortune on a boxful of tools before work can start. Practically all the furniture modifications and aids can be made with only eight hand tools. As there are no such things as good cheap tools, it is advisable to buy the best you can afford: tools made by a well-known company will last a lifetime, and if used and stored properly will not need to be sharpened too often. Always keep tools well out of a child's reach.

The tools required are:

Handsaw, 10 PPI
Back or Tenon Saw, 250 mm (10″)
Coping Saw
Junior or Mini Hacksaw
Hammer, approx 8 oz
Screwdriver suitable for No 6 screws
Hand Drill and a set of Twist Drills
Plane, preferably with replaceable blades if you are not good at sharpening on a stone
Flexible Rule, 2 metres, giving both metric and imperial measurements.

HOW TO USE YOUR TOOLS

Sawing

The handsaw is used for cutting large pieces of wood such as sheets of plywood, wooden planks and sections.

The back saw or tenon saw should only be used for cutting small pieces of wood such as battens and narrow pieces of plywood.

Both of these saws make a cut that is smooth enough to be finished with glasspaper. Do not hold these saws too tightly, or have the forefinger pointing down the blade like a child pretending his hand is a gun. Use the handsaw at an angle of about 45°, but when using the tenon saw start the cut at a slight angle, then slowly flatten it and saw straight across the wood.

The coping saw is used for cutting out shapes such as circles and curves. When it is used as a fret saw, the teeth should be pointing towards the handle, but when used to cut a small piece of wood on a bench hook, the blade must be turned round so that the teeth point away from the handle.

The junior or mini hacksaw is intended for cutting thin pieces of metal, such as nails or thick wire, and should only be used when the metal is held in a vice. It can also be used for cutting wooden dowel and small pieces of wood, plywood and plastic.

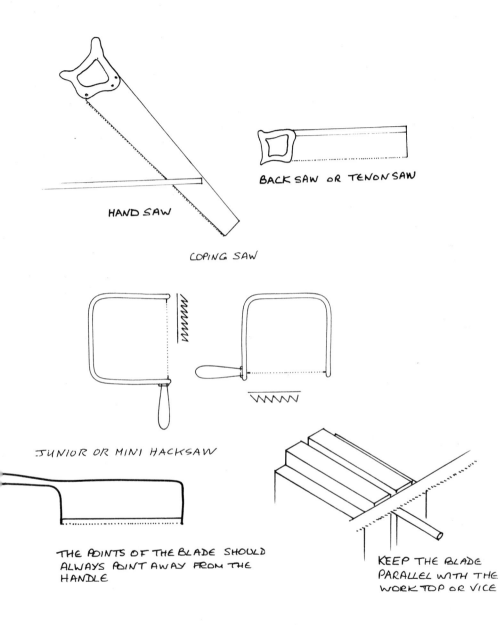

HAND SAW

BACK SAW OR TENON SAW

COPING SAW

JUNIOR OR MINI HACKSAW

THE POINTS OF THE BLADE SHOULD
ALWAYS POINT AWAY FROM THE
HANDLE

KEEP THE BLADE
PARALLEL WITH THE
WORK TOP OR VICE

9

Nailing

As no big nails are used in making the various items in this book, a hammer weighing about 250 g (8 oz) is quite heavy enough. Always hold the hammer by the end of the handle and learn to strike the nail squarely so that the nail will not bend. Regularly check the face of the hammer to ensure that it is clean and very smooth, as this will also help to stop the hammer head from slipping off the nail and bending it.

Grip the nail firmly between the thumb and forefinger.

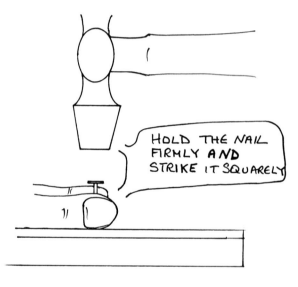

HOLD THE NAIL FIRMLY AND STRIKE IT SQUARELY

WIRE OR FRENCH NAIL

OVAL WIRE NAIL

PANEL PIN

Screwing

Screwdrivers come in many shapes and sizes and it is important to pick the one which fits the screw slot properly; if it does not, there is a good chance of the slot being damaged and left dangerously sharp. It is therefore a good idea to buy a set of screwdrivers which will cover most screw sizes. Another way of damaging the slot, so that it becomes dangerous, is to fail to keep the screwdriver upright. When this happens, it is not unusual for a thin and very sharp sliver of metal to be left sticking up.

Always counter-bore when using countersunk screws, so that the head is always flush with or slightly below the surface. There is no need to do this if brass cups are used.

Drilling

When using a hand drill or twist drill, do not apply too much pressure; let the drill do the cutting. The most important thing to learn is to keep the drill at 90° to the job. A twist drill is used to make a hole exactly the size and depth required. A special masonry drill will be necessary if holes have to be made in brick walls, breeze blocks and concrete. It is advisable to employ an expert for drilling some materials, such as glass and ceramic tiles.

When fixing something to a solid wall, it is best to buy specially made plugs which are tapped into a drilled hole so that, in effect, it is like driving a screw into a piece of wood. Advice on which type to use can be obtained from the local hardware shop.

A countersink bit is used to open up a hole so that the head of the screw is level with the surface or very slightly below it.

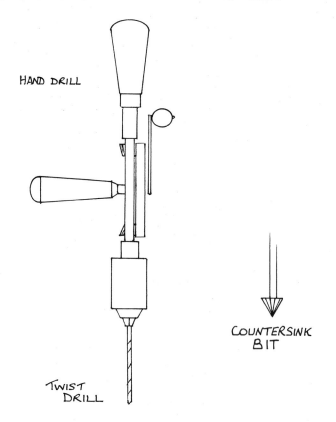

HAND DRILL

TWIST
DRILL

COUNTERSINK
BIT

Planing

The types of saw listed in the tool kit have been chosen because they do not leave the wood too rough, and a glasspaper finish is possible; but sometimes cheap off-cuts will need planing. As this is where you will save money, it is a good idea to learn how to use a plane.

One-handed planing is possible after a little practice. The wood is held upright and pressed against the glasspaper board batten as shown in the drawing. If you have a vice to hold the wood, then both hands should be used to grip the plane. At the start of the cut, apply a little extra pressure to the front handle—then even pressure with both hands until just before you reach the end of the wood, when a little extra pressure is applied to the back of the plane.

Always make sure that you plane with the grain of the wood and keep the blade sharp.

ADJUST THE BLADE
TO ONLY PEEP THROUGH.
THIS WILL MAKE VERY
THIN SHAVINGS.

HOLD THE WOOD UPRIGHT
WITH ONE HAND AND
PLANE WITH THE OTHER

IF YOU HAVE NO WORKSHOP

If you have no workshop, garage or spare room to work in, your kitchen can be temporarily converted into one. A quick and easy way to solve the problem is to make the work top the first job. It not only protects the table and gives a firm base to work on, but it makes the job of clearing and putting everything away quick and simple. The work top makes kitchen table carpentry possible.

The second job is to make a kitchen chair into a saw horse on which to cut larger pieces of wood. The seat top gives protection to the seat of the chair while you are sawing. If possible, choose a strong chair and one low enough for you to rest your knee on comfortably.

The third item to make is the bench hook which will provide a firm base on which to saw small bits of wood. This piece of equipment can be used on the work top.

Finally, make a few glasspaper boards for various grades of paper and some glasspaper sticks in a range of sizes and shapes.

Now, with the tools, some glue, nails and screws your workshop is ready for action.

WORK TOP

Shopping List
A. Base: plywood 9 mm, minimum size 300 mm × 500 mm (12″ × 20″)
B. Batten: softwood 25 mm × 25 mm × 500 mm (1″ × 1″ × 20″)
C. One thin cork tile

Construction: Glue and Nail

Instructions

1. Fix batten B to base A.
2. Cut cork tile into 25 mm (1″) strips, and glue to underside of the base and the inside edge of the batten.

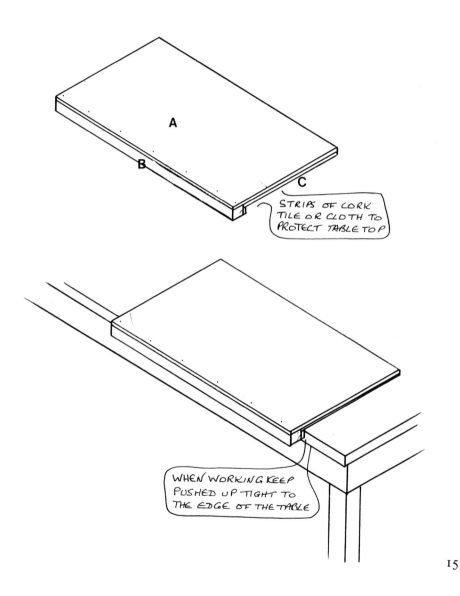

STRIPS OF CORK TILE OR CLOTH TO PROTECT TABLE TOP

WHEN WORKING KEEP PUSHED UP TIGHT TO THE EDGE OF THE TABLE

SEAT TOP

Shopping List

A. Seat Cover: plywood 9 mm × width of chair seat plus 50 mm (2″) × depth of chair plus 25 mm (1″)

B. Battens, 3 wanted: softwood 25 mm × 25 mm (1″ × 1″) × length to suit chair seat size.

Construction: Glue and Nail

Instructions

1. Fix battens B to the three sides of the seat cover A so that it makes an easy fit over the chair seat.
2. Glue cloth to the underside to give added protection to the chair seat.

BATTENS ON
THREE SIDES
ONLY

CLOTH TO PROTECT
CHAIR SEAT

THE SEAT TOP
SHOULD BE A
GOOD SNUG FIT

BENCH HOOK

Shopping List
A.   Base: plywood 9 mm × 180 mm × 300 mm (7″ × 12″)
B.   Wood Rest: softwood 40 mm × 40 mm × 130 mm ($1\frac{1}{2}″ × 1\frac{1}{2}″ × 5″$)
C.   Edge: softwood 25 mm × 25 mm × 180 mm (1″ × 1″ × 7″)

Construction: Glue and Nail

Instructions
1.   Fix wood rest B to base A as shown on drawing.
2.   Fix edge C to underside of base A.

FOR THE LEFT HANDED LEAVE THE GAP THIS SIDE

B

A

C

IF NOT USED ON WORK TOP GLUE ON CLOTH TO PROTECT TABLE

GLASSPAPER BOARDS AND STICKS

For many smoothing jobs it is better to rub the wood on the glasspaper than the glasspaper on the wood. The finish of the piece of plywood or softwood will be smoother and more square when it has been rubbed on a sheet of glasspaper glued to a piece of plywood, because only the high spots will come into contact with the rough cutting surface of the paper. Buy only good quality glasspaper and, to maintain a good cutting surface, keep it free of wood dust by regular brushing. Make several boards so that a range of grades of glasspaper are always ready for use.

Shopping List
A.   Base: plywood 4 mm × 230 mm × 305 mm (9″ × 12″)
B.   Battens, 2 wanted: softwood 25 mm × 25 mm × 305 mm
       (1″ × 1″ × 12″)
C.   Glasspaper: a range of grades

Construction: Glue and Nail

Instructions
1.   Fix battens B to base A.
2.   Glue glasspaper to each side, using only a very thin coat of glue.

Glasspaper sticks can be made in a wide range of shapes and sizes. Glue various grades of glasspaper to the wood, using only a very thin coat of glue.

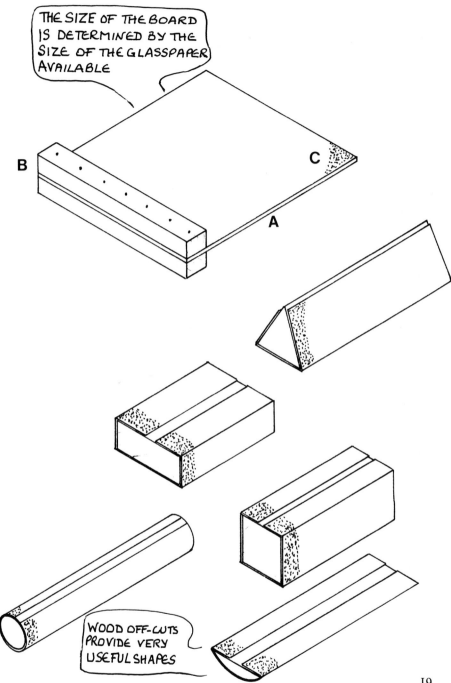

THE SIZE OF THE BOARD IS DETERMINED BY THE SIZE OF THE GLASSPAPER AVAILABLE

B

C

A

WOOD OFF-CUTS PROVIDE VERY USEFUL SHAPES

19

METHODS OF CONSTRUCTION

As it can safely be assumed that most people have used, or can learn to use, a hammer and a screwdriver, the three methods of construction chosen throughout this book are based on these fundamental skills: glue and nail, glue and screw and screw and nut. The latter is not used very often.

Study the drawings of the first two methods carefully before you start work.

Glue and Nail Construction

Glueing and nailing two or more pieces of wood together gives a very strong joint, so long as the pieces to be joined are free of paint and oil, are smooth, flat and touch one another throughout their whole length.

Use a glue of a well-known brand; apply it evenly and not too thickly to both sides to be joined. Wipe off surplus glue before it has had time to dry.

Always fully support wood before using the hammer. And **never** leave any nails sticking out of the wood. Use a nail punch to knock the nail heads so that they are just below the surface. If they are knocked deeper the little holes can be filled before painting.

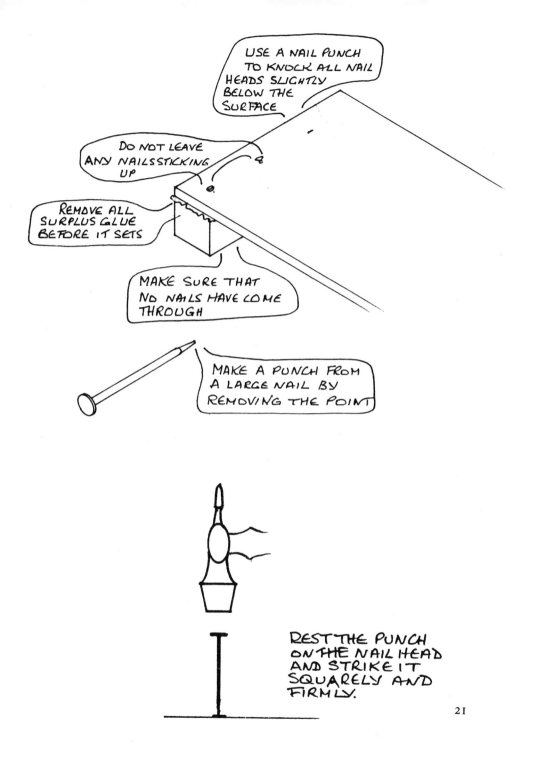

Glue and Screw Construction

As it is easy to remove screws, this method of construction is used when adjustments may have to be made. No glue is used for the trial assembly.

1. Drill a hole in one piece of wood A which the screw will only just go through.
2. Countersink the hole so that the screw head will be slightly below the surface.
3. Drill a hole in the other piece of wood B, half the diameter of the first one, and half the depth of the screw thread.
4. Screw the two pieces of wood together, but not so hard that the wood round the screw thread cracks—which would make the screw keep turning, and the joint insecure. For final assembly apply glue before screwing together.

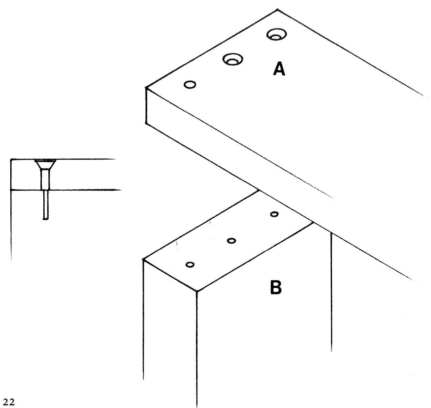

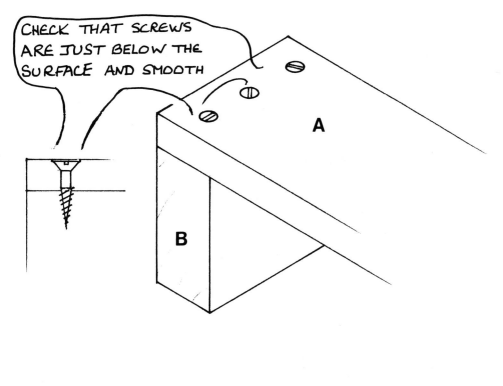

GLUES

Modern glues are so good that it is now much easier for the DIY enthu-
siast, as well as the kitchen table carpenter, to make things. Many jobs
can be successfully completed without having to make those difficult
joints, such as mortise and tenon and dovetails, which not only take
time to make but if not accurately cut will not be very strong. In this
book it is suggested that those who do not have the skills or the equipment should either glue and nail or glue and screw. Sometimes it is
only necessary to glue and clamp. If the finished job has to be washed
a lot or left outside it is better to use a waterproof glue such as boat
builders use.

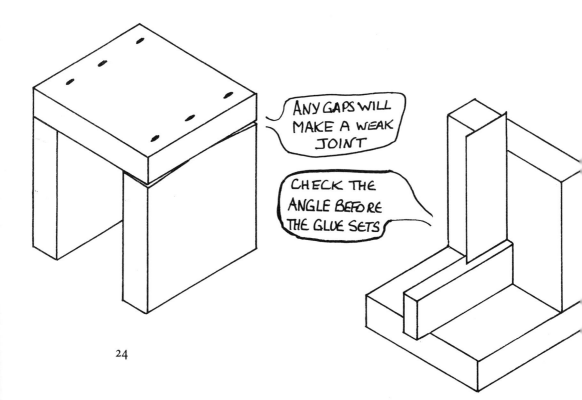

PAINTING

Most local paint suppliers carry a wide range of colours, and some even have special machines which will mix almost any shade required while you wait. It is essential that all modifications to furniture and aids that you make or get made are painted or stained, so that they do not stand out too much and so advertise the fact that a person is elderly.

Besides choice of colour, you will also have to decide which type of paint you buy—oil bound or water based. The latter is by far the easier to use. No expensive solvents are needed and small changes in colour can be made by adding a little water colour paint, so you have no excuse for not having a very good match.

As with tools, there is no such thing as a cheap paint brush, so buy the best you can afford. If you use water based paint, the brushes can be washed under a running cold water tap.

Painting and finishing is done in four stages:

1. Fill all holes, surface blemishes, cracks and corners that could become dirt traps with a proprietary filler, plastic wood, or putty. Allow plenty of time to dry, if possible overnight. There are two basic types of filler to choose from: those bought in powder form, to which water is added to make a putty-like mixture, and those supplied ready mixed in cans or plastic tubes. It is a good idea to make filling and painting jobs the last task before packing up for the day, to give plenty of drying time.
2. Rub down the whole surface to be painted, including the removal of all sharp corners and edges, with glasspaper, starting with a coarse grade and finishing with a fine one.
3. Apply two *thin* coats of the under paint, rubbing down with a fairly fine glasspaper between each coat.
4. Apply two *thin* top coats, again rubbing down between each coat.

Painting is not as difficult as most people think, and if the procedures just described are adhered to, three major problems will be eliminated.

1. Runs, like little rivers, down the wood which will take a very long time to dry and are then difficult to remove.
2. Drips on the floor.
3. Long waits while the paint dries.

Always stir the paint well before starting to use it, unless it is of the non-drip variety. Dip the brush only 12 mm ($\frac{1}{2}$") into the paint and wipe off any excess on the lip of the can.
Read the manufacturer's instructions and keep to them.

Staining

Much furniture is coloured and polished so that the wood's grain can be seen. In order to match this finish a stain must be used. There is a wide range of both water and spirit based stains on the market but the easiest to use is probably the water based one which can be bought in powder form. If the manufacturer's instructions are followed to the letter a good match can be obtained. Finish with a clear varnish.

KITCHEN

As so much time has to be spent in the kitchen, and much of it on your feet, changes should be made so that it becomes an easier place to work in. This may mean some fairly big alterations, but it will be well worth the short upheaval while they are being made. For example, shelves can be lowered, as can cabinets which are screwed to the wall.

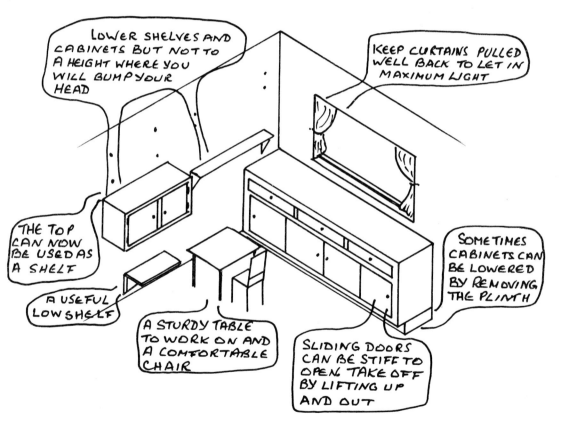

WORK TOP

This very useful working surface will not move away from you while it is being used. As it is so light and has a good edge to grip it can easily be carried to any room in the house and used on any table, even though it is mainly intended for kitchen use. It will not matter how dirty it gets, just take it to the sink for washing.

Shopping List
A. Tray: plywood 4 mm × 250 mm × 460 mm (10″ × 18″)
B. Batten: softwood 25 mm × 25 mm × 460 mm (1″ × 1″ × 18″)
C. Batten: softwood 12 mm × 25 mm × 460 mm ($\frac{1}{2}$″ × 1″ × 18″)
D. Formica or similar plastic sheet: 240 mm × 460 mm ($9\frac{1}{2}$ × 18″)

Construction: Glue and Nail

Instructions
1. Fix batten B to underside of tray A.
2. Fix batten C to top edge of tray A.
3. Glue plastic sheet to top of tray A with contact glue.

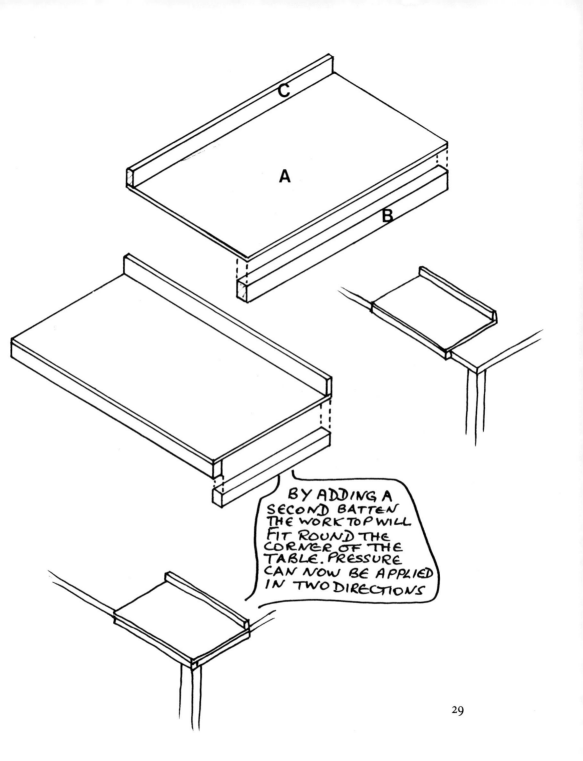

BY ADDING A SECOND BATTEN THE WORK TOP WILL FIT ROUND THE CORNER OF THE TABLE. PRESSURE CAN NOW BE APPLIED IN TWO DIRECTIONS

FOOT STOOL

Putting on shoes and socks, tying laces and cutting toe nails need not be such an effort if you can put your foot up on a little angled stool. It can be made to almost any height and it is up to you to decide how high after doing a few tests. If both feet are going to be put on the stool together, double the width.

Shopping List
A.   Board: softwood 15 mm × 125 mm × 230 mm ($\frac{5}{8}'' \times 5'' \times 9''$)
B.   Front Riser: softwood 15 mm × 125 mm × 150 mm ($\frac{5}{8}'' \times 5'' \times 6''$)
C.   Back Riser: softwood 15 mm × 125 mm × 50 mm ($\frac{5}{8}'' \times 5'' \times 2''$)

Construction: Glue and Nail

Instructions
1.   Fix front riser B to board A.
2.   Fix back riser C to board A.
3.   Glasspaper and paint.

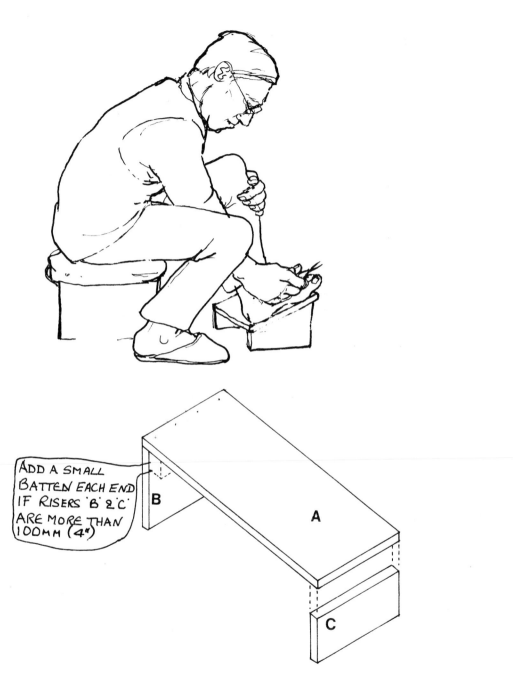

ADD A SMALL
BATTEN EACH END
IF RISERS 'B' & 'C'
ARE MORE THAN
100MM (4")

B

A

C

31

WHEELED TROLLEY

A wheeled trolley can be pushed to where it is needed. The sizes given are guide dimensions only and should be changed to make the trolley just right for you. You may find later that you need another one—one for the kitchen for dishes, knives and other gadgets which you find you need for preparing food, the second in the living room to hold all the things for daily living, including hobbies and other pastimes.

Two methods of construction are suggested and both give good results. Little plastic blocks made from nylon are available from DIY shops and stores and these can be used instead of wooden battens.

Shopping List

A. Top: plywood 6 mm × 250 mm × 600 mm (10″ × 24″)
B. Sides, 2 wanted: plywood 6 mm × 250 mm × 600 mm (10″ × 24″)
C. Shelf: plywood 6 mm × 200 mm × 600 mm (8″ × 24″)
D. Base: plywood 6 mm × 250 mm × 600 mm (10″ × 24″)
E. Shelf Front, 3 wanted: plywood 6 mm × 40 mm × 600 mm (1½″ × 24″)
F. Shelf Back Small: plywood 6 mm × 44 mm × 600 mm (1¾″ × 24″)
G. Back: plywood 6 mm × 563 mm × 600 mm (22 3/16″ × 24″)
H. Cup Hooks, 5 or 6 wanted
I. Plastic Blocks, about 28 wanted
                            or
    Softwood Battens cut from 450 cm × 20 mm × 20 mm (15ft × ¾″ × ¾″)
J. Screws for plastic blocks. Get advice from supplier, about 80 wanted
K. Castors, 4 wanted: Wheel size about 50 mm (2″) diameter

Construction: Wooden battens—glue and nail
Plastic blocks—wood screws

Instructions
1. Fix battens or plastic blocks to parts A, C, D and G as illustrated.
2. Assemble as illustrated.
3. Glasspaper thoroughly.
4. Fix castors in the corners of base D.
5. Finish by painting or staining.

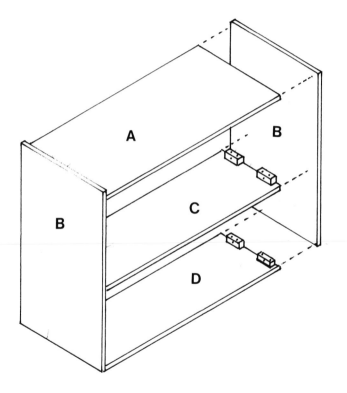

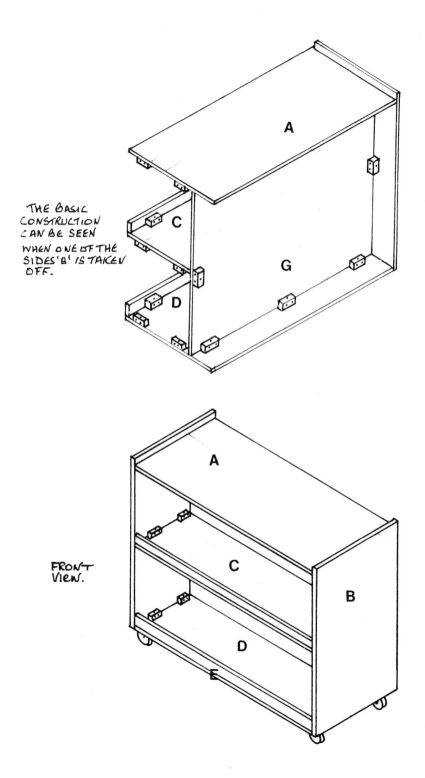

THE BASIC
CONSTRUCTION
CAN BE SEEN

WHEN ONE OF THE
SIDES 'B' IS TAKEN
OFF.

A

C

G

D

FRONT
VIEW.

A

C

B

D

E

34

NYLON BLOCK
OR
PLYWOOD AND
BATTEN
CONSTRUCTION

VIEW OF BACK
SHOWING HANGING
SPACE

35

PLINTH

The lower shelves and drawers of a number of pieces of furniture are often too low to be comfortably reached. The plinth is one item which should be made by a professional: he should also fix the furniture to it. If there is the slightest chance of it being unstable and falling on you when the doors or drawers are open, then he must fix it to the wall.

Never do any modifications to gas or electrical appliances yourself. The gas and electricity authorities have trained staff for this work and will be only too pleased to help and advise you.

It is not possible to give any dimensions as these will depend on the size and the weight the plinth will have to carry.

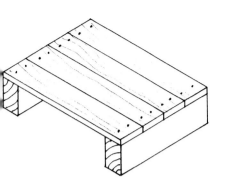

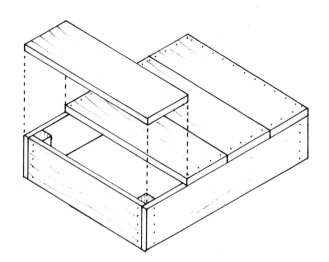

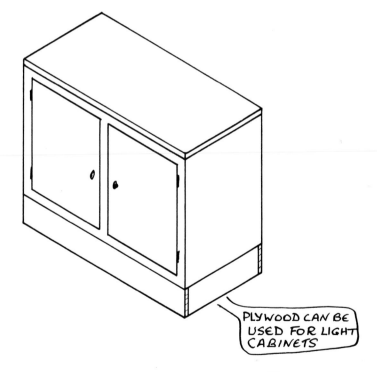

PLYWOOD CAN BE
USED FOR LIGHT
CABINETS

CUTTING AID AND BOARD

A useful little kitchen tool for cutting up, slicing and scraping. The size of the handle is important, so grip various pieces of dowel until one is found which feels comfortable when it is held tightly. Whatever handle size is finally decided upon, the nails should stick out about 50 mm (2″).

Shopping List
A.   Handle: wooden dowel, diameter and length to suit the hand
B.   Nails, 9 wanted
C.   Cutting Board: softwood about 15 mm × 150 mm × 150 mm ($\frac{5}{8}″ \times 6″ \times 6″$)

Instructions
1.   Mark out the positions for the nails.
2.   Drill the nine holes so that they are a drive fit for the nails.
3.   Hammer the nails through the handle A.
4.   Finish by glasspapering the ends of the handle and the cutting board C.

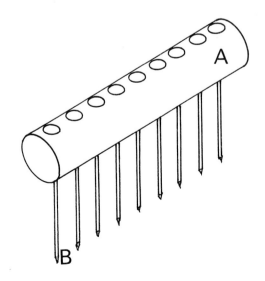

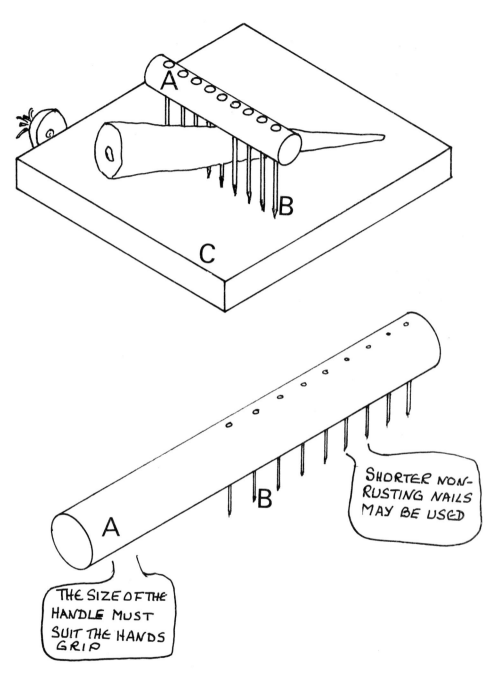

39

BREAD AND BUTTER SPREADER

If the butter is not too hard and the bread has not been cut too thin, then the job of buttering a slice of bread is made much easier.

Shopping List
A. Base Board: plywood 6 mm × 150 mm × 200 mm (6″ × 8″)
B. Table Batten: softwood 25 mm × 25 mm × 150 mm (1″ × 1″ × 6″)
C. Table Batten: softwood 25 mm × 25 mm × 175 mm (1″ × 1″ × 7″)
D. Bread Rest Battens, 2 wanted: 4 mm × 4 mm × 150 mm ($\frac{3}{16}″ × \frac{3}{16}″ × 6″$)

Construction: Glue and Nail

Instructions
1. Fix table batten B to base board A.
2. Fix table batten C to base board A.
3. Fix bread battens D to top of base board A.
4. Finish by glasspapering to remove all sharp corners and edges.

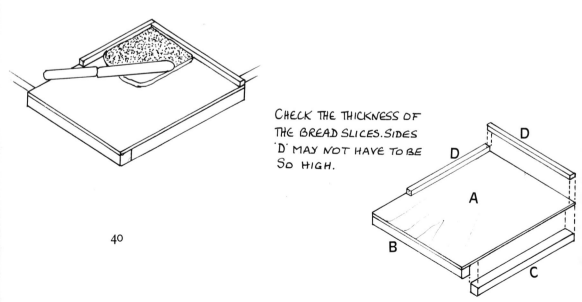

CHECK THE THICKNESS OF THE BREAD SLICES. SIDES 'D' MAY NOT HAVE TO BE SO HIGH.

CUTTING BOARD

This can be made in much the same way as the bread and butter spreader, except that it has spikes to hold the food. The position of the spikes can be changed if they do not hold the food firmly enough. Do not make the spikes too long—usually 25 mm (1″) is enough. If nails are used, make sure that they are well dried after washing to prevent rusting, or better still use non-rusting nails.

Shopping List
A.   Base Board: plywood 6 mm × 200 mm × 200 mm (8″ × 8″)
B.   Base Batten: softwood 25 mm × 25 mm × 200 mm (1″ × 1″ × 8″)
C.   Base Batten: softwood 25 mm × 25 mm × 175 mm (1″ × 1″ × 7″)
D.   Spikes, 9 wanted: nails about 30 mm (1¼″) long and heavy gauge

Construction: Glue and Nail

Instructions
1.   Drill 9 holes as illustrated. These must be much smaller than the diameter of the spikes D.
2.   Fix base batten B to base board A.
3.   Fix base batten C to base board A.
4.   Hammer the spikes D from the under side of the base board A.
5.   Glasspaper to finish.

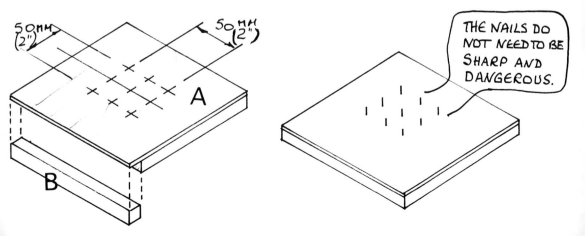

KITCHEN TABLE WORKING SURFACE

A lot of time is spent in the kitchen preparing food, so it is very important to make sure that the kitchen table is made an easy place to work on. If this is done, preparing food will become much less tiring and then there is no excuse for not being more adventurous with your diet and cooking those dishes you used to enjoy so much. The working surface can be made any size or shape and, should the table be too high, fit it underneath as illustrated. In the interests of hygiene, the top and sides should have a hard plastic surface such as Formica. Several variations can be made, as shown in the illustrations.

Shopping List for Work Surface (guide sizes)
A.   Board: plywood 9 mm × 400 mm × 400 mm (16″ × 16″)
B.   Screws and wing nuts, 2 wanted: buy plated ones. The length will depend on the thickness of the table top. Dome topped screws are easier to clean.

Shopping List for Underneath Work Surface (guide sizes)
A.   Board: plywood 9 mm × 400 mm × 400 mm (16″ × 16″)
B.   Sides, 2 wanted: softwood 15 mm × 50 mm × 150 mm ($\frac{5}{8}$″ × 2″ × 6″). The width of the sides determines how low the work surface will be.

Instructions for Work Surface
1.   Drill holes for screws 50 mm (2″) in from sides and 50 mm (2″) in from the back of board A.
2.   Drill holes in table top 100 mm (4″) from front edge.
3.   Fix work surface to table, allowing an overlap of about 100 mm (4″).

Instructions for Underneath Work Surface
1.   Fix sides B to board A with non-rusting wood screws.
2.   Carefully drill table so that the screws will be in the centre of sides B and 30 mm ($1\frac{1}{4}$″) from each end.
3.   Paint sides B and fix to table with long non-rusting screws.

DRILL HOLES FOR FIXING TO TABLE

A

FOR A LOWER BOARD FIX UNDERNEATH

A

B

43

MIXING BOARD

This board will hold a mixing bowl firmly while you are mixing all types of ingredients with a spoon, a hand mixing machine or an electric hand-held mixing machine. If a Formica topped board is used it is better to have the holes cut professionally, but if you do the job use a fine blade to help prevent chipping. Cut edges can be protected by ironing on edging strip: this is bought in small reels.

Shopping List
A. Board: plywood 9 mm × 355 mm × 355 mm (14″ × 14″)
B. Screw and Nut, 2 wanted: dome headed are the easiest to keep clean

Construction: Screw and Nut

Instructions
1. Measure diameter of bowls just under the rim.
2. Mark out and cut holes for bowls so that they are 40 mm (1½″) in from the sides and the same distance from the front edge.
3. Drill holes in board A for screws.
4. Glasspaper and paint.

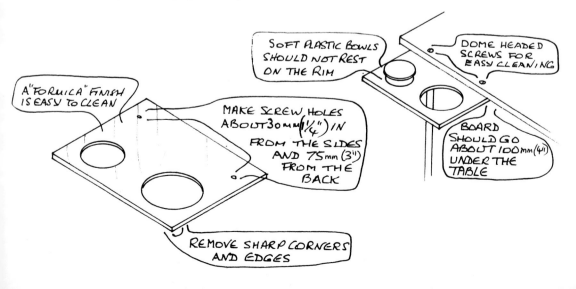

FLOUR

SHOE OR BOOT REMOVER

A small aid which will give a little more independence and save that struggle when trying to get the shoes off—and an even greater struggle when rubber boots are involved. The 'V' shaped cut-out may have to be made bigger if it is to be used for getting off men's large sizes.

Shopping List
A.   Board: softwood 15 mm × 135 mm × 400 mm ($\frac{5}{8}$″ × $5\frac{1}{4}$″ × 16″)
B.   Riser: softwood 15 mm × 50 mm × 135 mm ($\frac{5}{8}$″ × 2″ × $5\frac{1}{4}$″)

Construction: Glue and Nail

Instructions
1.   Cut out board A as illustrated.
2.   Fix riser B so that it does not touch the 'V' cut-out.
3.   Glasspaper and remove all corners.

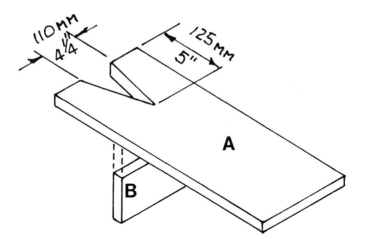

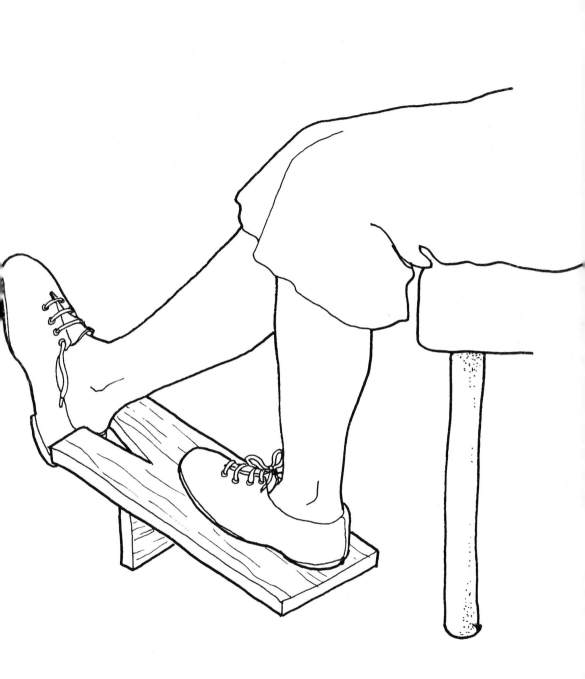

HOBBY WORK TOP

As you grow older the garage and the garden shed seem to be too cold to work in as the summer comes to an end. It is possible to do some work or enjoy a hobby using the kitchen table if you make a hobby work top. The size of the working area can be made larger or smaller, depending on the kind of work you want to do. Should you wish to fix a vice to the work top, make the table edge batten wide enough to take the vice clamp. See illustration.

Shopping List
A. Base: plywood 9 mm × 450 mm × 630 mm (18″ × 25″)
B. Table Edge: softwood 25 mm × 25 mm × 630 mm (1″ × 1″ × 25″)
C. Top Edge: softwood 12 mm × 50 mm × 630 mm ($\frac{1}{2}$″ × 2″ × 25″)
D. Sides, 2 wanted: softwood 12 mm × 50 mm × 100 mm
    ($\frac{1}{2}$″ × 2″ × 4″)

Construction: Glue and Nail

Instructions
1. Fix table edge B to base A.
2. Fix top edge C to base A.
3. Cut an angle on sides D.
4. Fix sides D to base A.

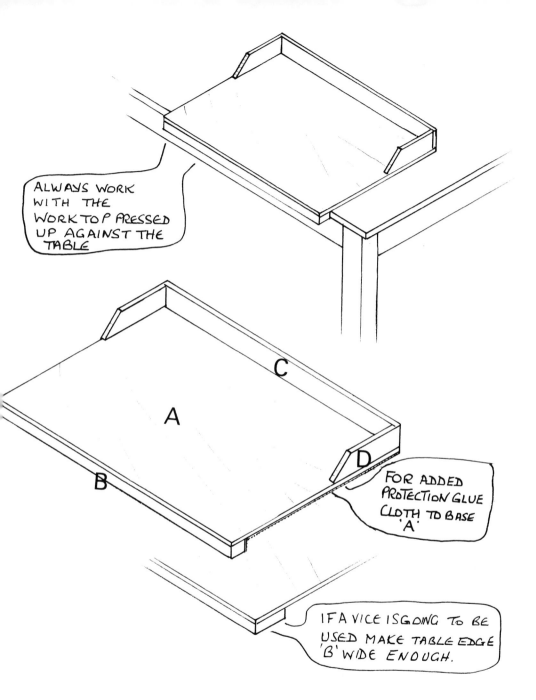

49

APRONS

An apron, tailor-made, with pockets the right size and in the right place, will make it possible to move around the home with all the bits and pieces needed and still have the hands free. Carefully design the size and shape of the pockets so that the hands can easily get into them, and at the same time make sure that the articles to be carried will fit and not fall out when the person bends over. Several aprons should be made and used for various purposes.

Shopping List
A.   Cloth: guide size only 600 mm × 700 mm (24″ × 28″)
B.   Tapes: about 2 metres (2 yards)

Instructions
1.   Measure the person and make pattern.
2.   Cut out cloth A and hem edges.
3.   Sew on pockets. Don't make them too big or they will fall open.
4.   Sew on tapes.

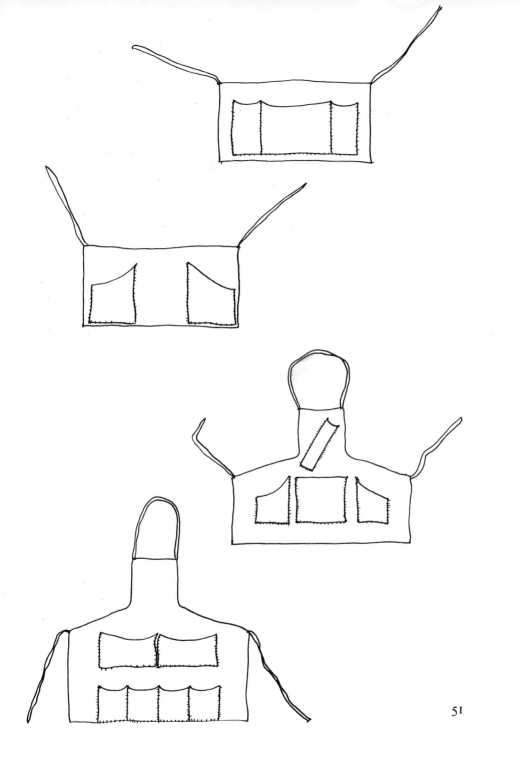

51

BANDOLIER

Those who do not want to be cluttered up with an apron may find the bandolier a better option for use indoors and in the garden. Any size of pocket can be made, and if the angle is right, no difficulty will be found in using them.

The bandolier must be made left or right handed and the length will depend on the size of the person who is to wear it.

Shopping List
A. Cloth: canvas or strong cloth, guide size for three pockets 255 mm × 635 mm (10″ × 25″)
B. Hook: bent from stiff wire
C. Ring: small curtain ring or bend from stiff wire

Instructions
1. Fold cloth in half lengthwise and sew three pockets.
2. Cut the angle of the pockets.
3. Sew pocket side.
4. Cut the ends to a point and sew.
5. Fix string and hook to top end.
6. Fix ring to lower end.
7. Adjust string length.

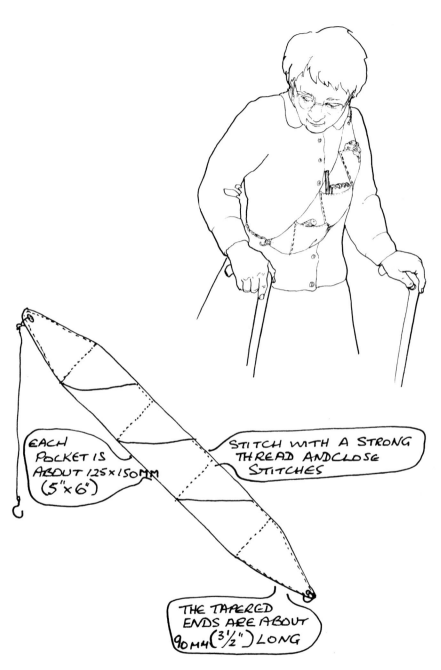

EACH POCKET IS ABOUT 125×150MM (5"×6")

STITCH WITH A STRONG THREAD AND CLOSE STITCHES

THE TAPERED ENDS ARE ABOUT 90MM (3½") LONG

PLASTIC SACK AND SHEET APRONS

Plastic aprons can be quite expensive, but these are cheap enough to be 'throw aways'. Pockets can be stuck on with good quality insulation tape.

DINING ROOM AND SITTING ROOM

The sitting room or the sitting area of the dining/sitting room must be made draught free, warm and light. It is not always easy to achieve, but every effort has to be made if you are really to enjoy your leisure hours. Draughts seem to invade a room from the most unlikely places, but they have to be found. After checking windows and doors, look for places where gas pipes come through the floor and, while on your knees, make sure cold air is not coming up through any gaps between the boards.

Don't leave carpets down which do not lie perfectly flat on the floor. If there are badly worn edges and threadbare patches which could trip you up, try turning the carpet round so that they are hidden under furniture or in places where you do not walk. Don't polish under carpets and mats.

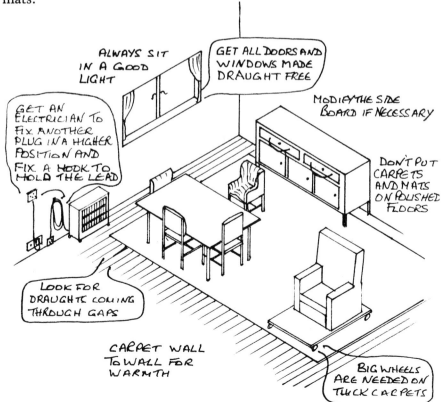

WOODEN CHAIR MODIFICATIONS

There are many modifications which can be made to wooden dining and kitchen chairs which will help you to sit more comfortably at the table with the rest of the family. The following series of drawings show some of the things that can be done with 6 mm plywood. It is important to get a kitchen chair modified, as most of the food can then be prepared while sitting down.

As most chairs are made from a hardwood it will be necessary to drill pilot holes for the screws.

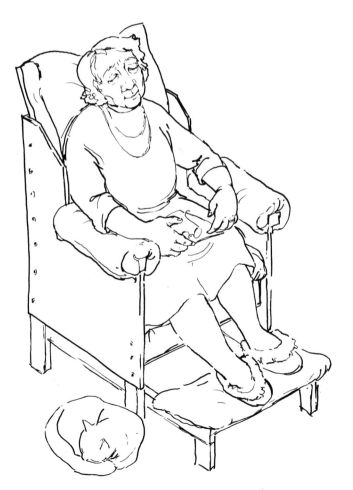

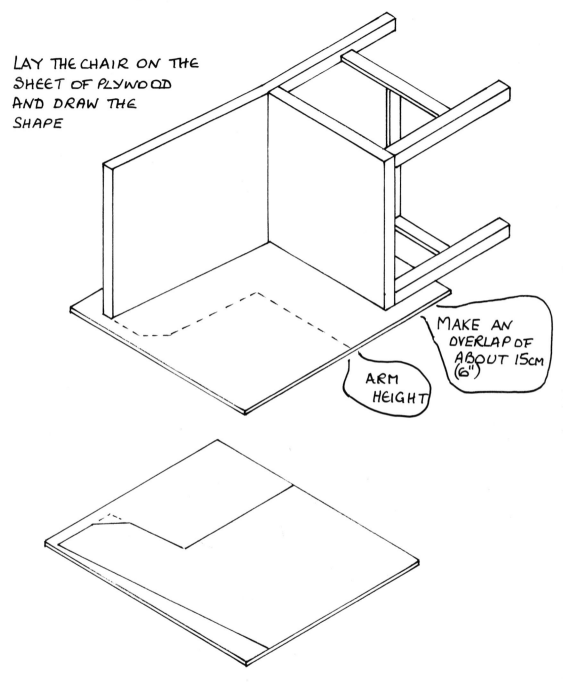

LAY THE CHAIR ON THE
SHEET OF PLYWOOD
AND DRAW THE
SHAPE

ARM
HEIGHT

MAKE AN
OVERLAP OF
ABOUT 15CM
(6")

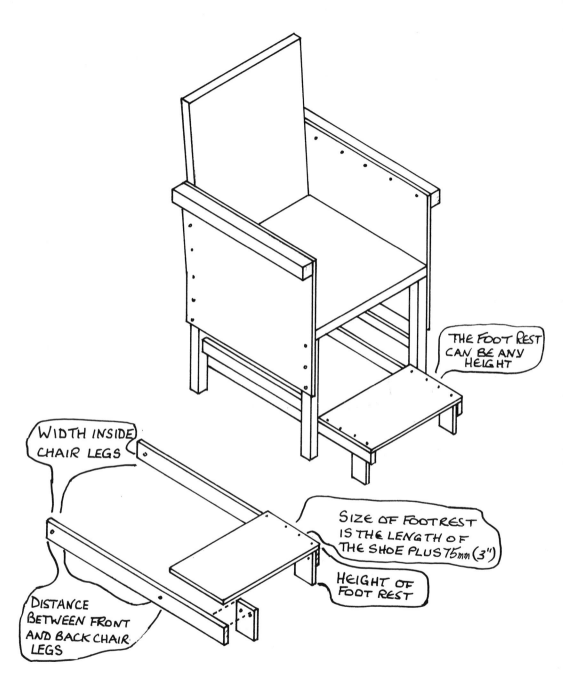

THE FOOT REST CAN BE ANY HEIGHT

WIDTH INSIDE CHAIR LEGS

SIZE OF FOOTREST IS THE LENGTH OF THE SHOE PLUS 75mm (3")

HEIGHT OF FOOT REST

DISTANCE BETWEEN FRONT AND BACK CHAIR LEGS

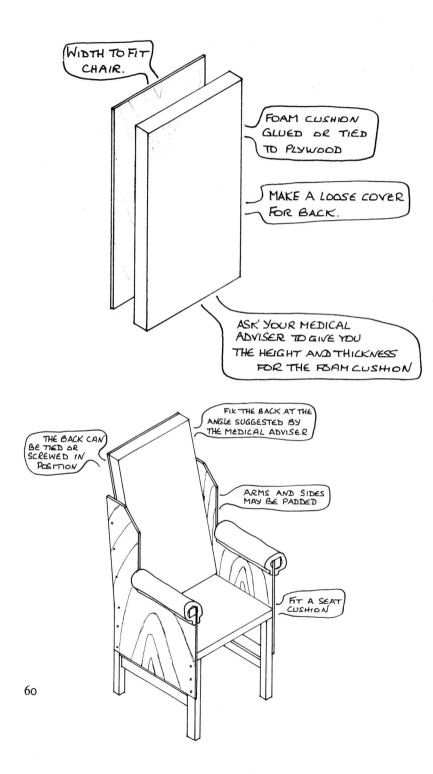

MODIFYING A METAL TUBE CHAIR

Chairs with metal frames can be modified in much the same way as wooden ones, the main difference being in how the panels are fixed. Nuts and bolts can be used, but only those of a small diameter because large holes in the tube weaken it. Self-tapping screws work well so long as the holes are made the correct size, and this information must be obtained when the screws are purchased. Only buy screws with a large diameter head which will not pull through the plywood.

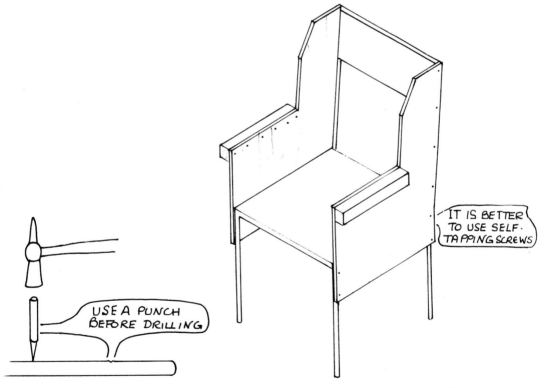

LARGE HOLES WILL WEAKEN THE TUBE.

CHAIR TROLLEY

Every effort must be made to make it possible for all the family to sit down together for meals, and this can often be done by making a wheeled trolley. It might be necessary sometimes to raise the foot rest area to make it more comfortable, and if it has to be pushed over thick carpets buy larger castors, say 50 mm (2″) diameter wheels.

Shopping List
A. Base Board: plywood, for sizes see illustration
B. Corner Battens, 8 wanted: softwood 25 mm × 25 mm × 75 mm (1″ × 1″ × 3″)
C. Castors
D. Corner Blocks, 4 wanted: plywood 9 mm × 65 mm × 65 mm (2½″ × 2½″)

Construction: Glue and Screw

Instructions
1. Fix corner battens to base board as illustrated.
2. Fix corner blocks to base board A.
3. Fix castors.
4. Glasspaper and paint.

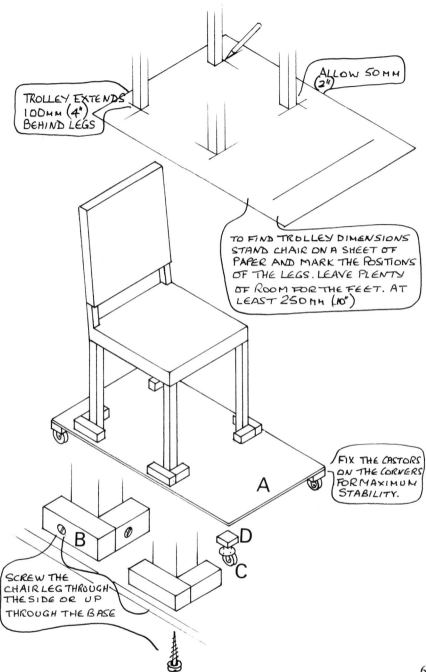

TROLLEY EXTENDS 100MM (4") BEHIND LEGS

ALLOW 50MM (2")

TO FIND TROLLEY DIMENSIONS STAND CHAIR ON A SHEET OF PAPER AND MARK THE POSITIONS OF THE LEGS. LEAVE PLENTY OF ROOM FOR THE FEET. AT LEAST 250MM (10")

FIX THE CASTORS ON THE CORNERS FOR MAXIMUM STABILITY.

A

B

D

C

SCREW THE CHAIR LEG THROUGH THE SIDE OR UP THROUGH THE BASE

63

CHAIR AND TABLE RAISERS

There is no good reason why you have to live with chairs and tables which are too low. They can all be raised to a better height by making the legs longer with raising blocks and, so long as they fit well and do not let the furniture feel insecure by even the slightest wobble, they will be used. Two types are illustrated—one can be fitted to wood or metal furniture but the other can only be used on wooden legs. Tubular steel chairs and tables can often be altered in height by buying metal tube which will just push over the leg. This tube can be cut to length, fitted over the existing leg, drilled and held in place by self-tapping screws. It is not possible to give any dimensions as these must be taken from the furniture and the height suggested by the medical adviser. Remember that the fit must be very good and do not make them too high, so causing the furniture to become unstable.

Shopping List
A.   The Box: good quality plywood about 9 mm thick
B.   Blocks: softwood. These must fit snugly in the box.
     Don't forget that 4 are wanted.

Instructions
1.   Measure the leg.
2.   Cut the plywood as illustrated.
3.   Make the box.
4.   Cut the block B to size.
5.   Glasspaper and paint.

THE EXTENSION TUBE SHOULD BE A GOOD FIT

TO PROTECT THE FLOOR FIT THE SAME TYPE OF TIPS AS USED ON STICKS.

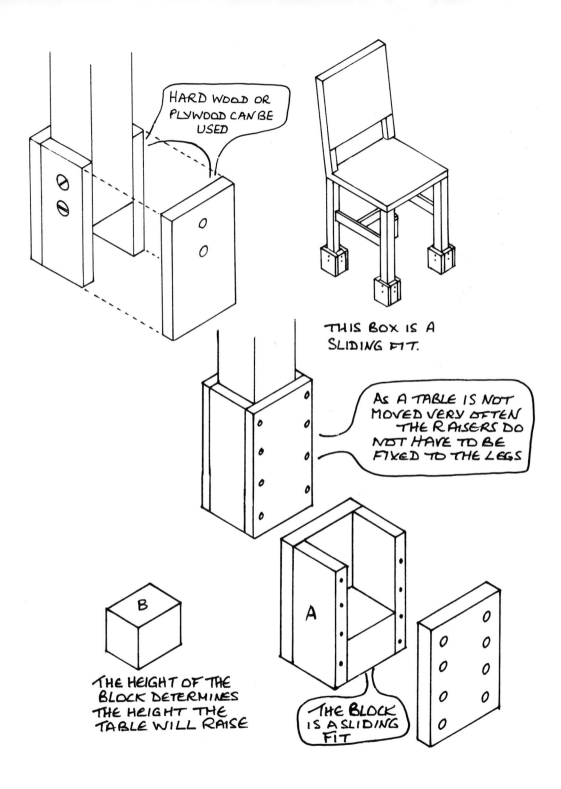

DRAUGHT SCREEN

Screens do not have to be very tall and heavy, especially if you are always going to be sitting down while being protected from draughts. A low screen can be made from two or three of the old type of clothes horse.

Shopping List for Each Panel
A. Uprights, 2 wanted: softwood 30 mm × 30 mm × 1500 mm ($1\frac{1}{4}'' × 1\frac{1}{4}'' × 60''$)
B. Dowels, 2 wanted: 12 mm diameter × 400 mm ($\frac{1}{2}''$ diameter × 16'')
C. Hinges, 2 wanted: ordinary hinges will do, but double action are better as the panels can be swung through 180°
D. Screen Covers: cloth or plastic

Instructions
1. Drill holes in uprights A 30 mm ($1\frac{1}{4}''$) from each end for dowels B.
2. Glue dowels B into uprights A. Lay on flat surface while the glue dries.
3. Fix the hinges C 50 mm (2'') from each end.
4. Glasspaper and paint.
5. Join panels together.
6. Fix on screen covers.

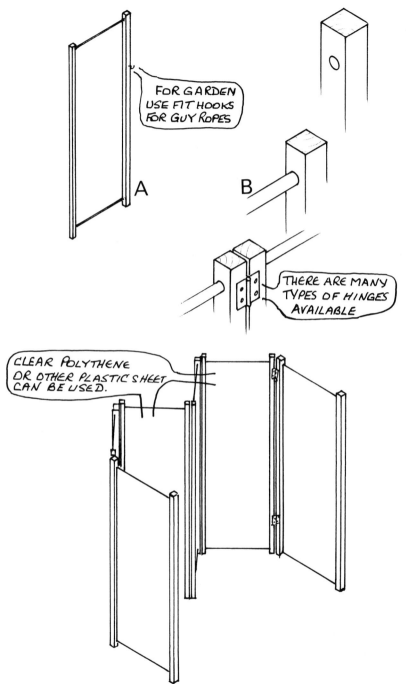

THE FAVOURITE ARMCHAIR

The armchair is one piece of furniture one grows to love, and over the years it seems to become more comfortable; the thought of it being replaced by something which is supposed to be better does not bear thinking about. The next few pages give details of how an armchair can be modified, in the hope that it will become an even greater friend and not have to be taken away. Discuss the problem with your medical adviser as he may have some more ideas.

BACK REST

This aid is only suitable for those chairs which have loose cushions as it fits underneath them. Armchairs vary in size so much that only a materials list can be given.

Shopping List
A.   Back: plywood 4 mm × height required × width of back cushion
B.   Cloth: strong piece of cloth the width of the back A × 350 mm (14″)
C.   Strings, 2 lengths wanted: strong cord about 2 metres (2 yards)

Instructions
1.   Cut off 2 corners of back A.
2.   Round all corners and edges with glasspaper.
3.   Sew loops to cloth B for strings C.
4.   Fix cloth B to back A with contact glue.
5.   Fix strings to cloth B.
6.   Put back A in chair at the required angle and tie to chair feet as illustrated.
7.   Replace cushions.

68

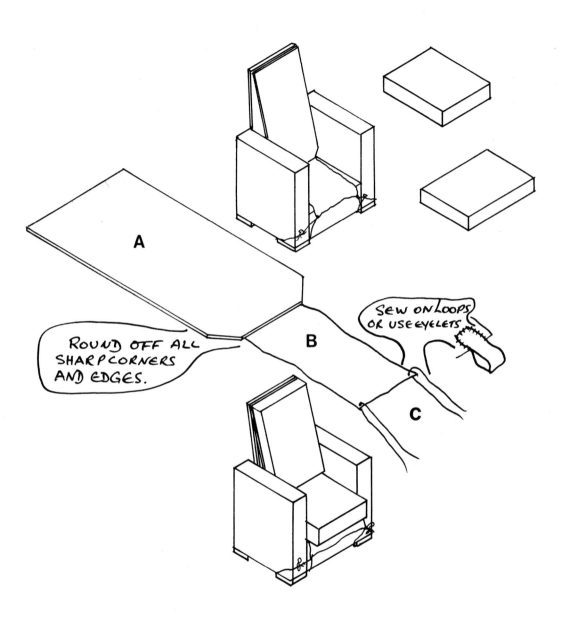

A

B

C

ROUND OFF ALL SHARP CORNERS AND EDGES.

SEW ON LOOPS OR USE EYELETS

LEG REST

Speak to your medical adviser about the height and angle he would like the leg to be kept at. Solid wood is better to use than plywood as it is less likely to bend under your weight.

Shopping List

A. Rest: softwood, minimum size 12 mm × 150 mm × length ($\frac{1}{2}'' \times 6'' \times$ length)

To calculate length, add together length of rest required to hold leg, plus a minimum of 200 mm (8″) which will be under the cushion.

B. Support: softwood, minimum size 12 mm × 150 mm ($\frac{1}{2}'' \times 6''$) × height required

C. Batten: softwood 30 mm × 30 mm × 150 mm ($1\frac{1}{4}'' \times 1\frac{1}{4}'' \times 6''$)

Construction: Glue and Nail

Instructions

1. Fix batten C to rest A.
2. Fix support B to rest A.
3. Glasspaper and paint or stain.
4. Upholster rest A.

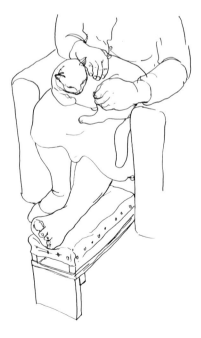

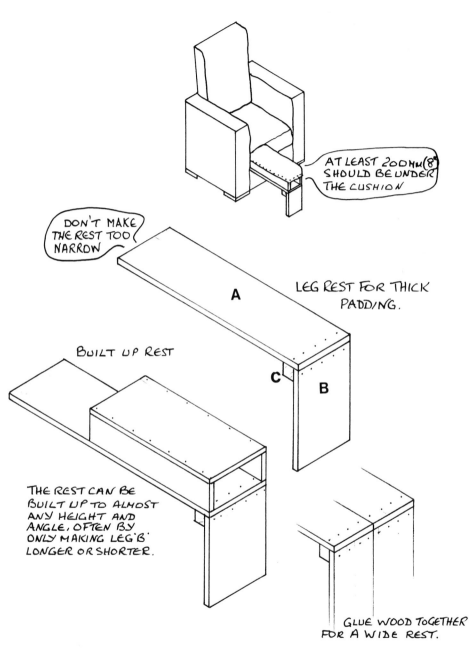

AT LEAST 200MM (8") SHOULD BE UNDER THE CUSHION

DON'T MAKE THE REST TOO NARROW

LEG REST FOR THICK PADDING.

A

C

B

BUILT UP REST

THE REST CAN BE BUILT UP TO ALMOST ANY HEIGHT AND ANGLE, OFTEN BY ONLY MAKING LEG 'B' LONGER OR SHORTER.

GLUE WOOD TOGETHER FOR A WIDE REST.

71

SHAPED LEG REST

This is another version of the leg rest which your medical adviser may prefer you to use. The upholstery on which your leg rests should completely cover the woodwork, so that there is no danger of the leg touching anything hard.

Shopping List
A. Rest: 9 mm plywood or 12 mm ($\frac{1}{2}''$) softwood × minimum width 150 mm (6")
B. Support: 9 mm plywood or 12 mm ($\frac{1}{2}''$) softwood × minimum width 150 mm (6")
C. Support Batten: softwood 30 mm × 30 mm × 150 mm minimum ($1\frac{1}{4}'' \times 1\frac{1}{4}'' \times 6''$ minimum)
D. Sides, 2 wanted: 9 mm plywood or softwood 12 mm ($\frac{1}{2}''$) × about 100 mm (4") × the amount of leg that has to be supported
E. Side Battens, 2 wanted: softwood 25 mm × 25 mm ($1'' \times 1''$)
F. Cloth and foam plastic for upholstery

Construction: Glue and Nail

Instructions
1. Fix support battens C to support B.
2. Fix side battens E to sides D.
3. Fix sides D to rest A.
4. Fix support B to rest A.
5. Glasspaper and paint.
6. Fix upholstery between sides D as illustrated.

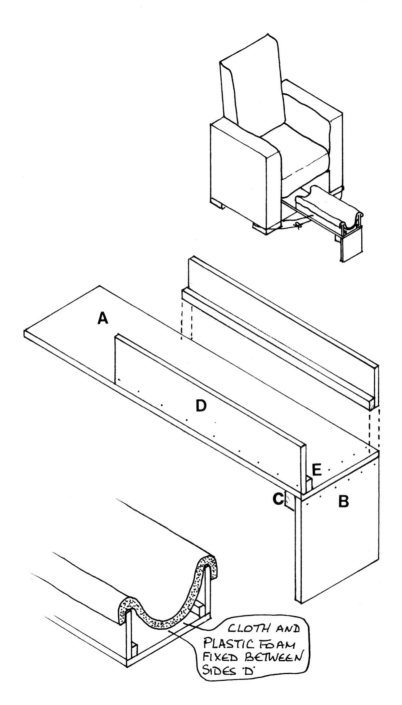

CLOTH AND PLASTIC FOAM FIXED BETWEEN SIDES 'D'

73

LEG REST EXTENSION

If you have one of these, you can 'put your feet up' whenever you feel like it. There is no need to fix the rest to the chair but if it does tend to move, it can always be tied to the chair's foot with a cord. The angle and length can be decided by your medical adviser, after which it will be possible to work out all the dimensions. Foam plastic for the upholstery can be bought from some shops cut to the exact size you want.

Shopping List
A. Top: plywood 4 mm
B. Sides, 2 wanted: plywood 4 mm
C. Side Batten Long, 2 wanted: 25 mm × 25 mm (1″ × 1″)
D. Side Batten Front, 2 wanted: 25 mm × 25 mm (1″ × 1″)
E. Side Batten Back, 2 wanted: 25 mm × 25 mm (1″ × 1″)
F. Back: plywood 4 mm
G. Front: plywood 4 mm
H. Foam plastic or other upholstery material
I. Cloth to cover padding

Construction: Glue and Nail

Instructions
1. Work out all the dimensions.
2. Cut out sides B.
3. Fix side battens long C to top edge of sides B.
4. Fix side battens front D to sides B.
5. Fix side battens back E to sides B.
6. Fix back F to assembled sides B.
7. Fix front G to assembled sides B.
8. Fix top A to sides.
9. Glasspaper and paint or stain.
10. Upholster top A.

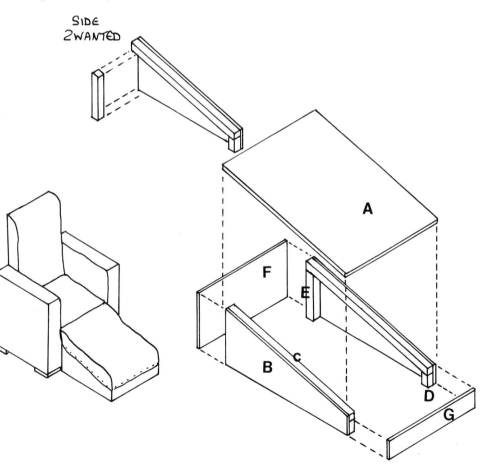

ARMCHAIR TRAY

This tray fits close to the body and is held in place by two elastic car roof rack straps. It can very quickly be removed in an emergency.

Shopping List
A.   Tray: plywood 6 mm × 460 mm × width of chair plus 100 mm ($18''$ × width of chair plus $4''$)

B.   Sides, 2 wanted: softwood 12 mm × 50 mm × 460 mm ($\frac{1}{2}'' × 2'' × 18''$)

C.   Tray Edge: softwood 12 mm × 50 mm × width of chair plus 100 mm ($\frac{1}{2}'' × 2''$ × width of chair plus $4''$)

Construction: Glue and Nail

Instructions
1.   Make cut out if required.
2.   Fix sides B to tray A.
3.   Fix tray edge C to tray A.
4.   Glasspaper and paint.
5.   Place on chair and find best position for eye screw (see illustration).
6.   Make elastic straps the right length.

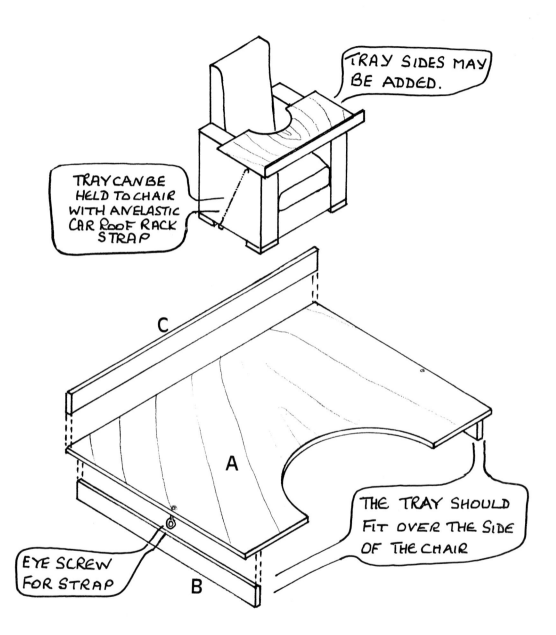

ARMCHAIR TROLLEY

What could be better than to be able easily to push or have your favourite armchair pushed about the room, so that you can sit in the sun on those lovely spring days or be able to get that little bit closer to the fire as winter comes. Two versions are given, one for very heavy chairs and the other for the lighter and often more modern ones.

Again, it is only possible to give the size of the materials to buy and not how much, as these chairs come in all shapes and sizes. Regarding the castors, don't buy those with very small wheels, particularly if they have to be used on thick-carpeted floors. Wheels of about 50 mm (2″) diameter are suitable for most homes.

Shopping List for Light Armchairs
A. Base: plywood 9 mm × width of chair plus 75 mm (3″) × length of chair plus 255 mm (10″) for footrest plus 75 mm (3″)
B. Strengthening Strip, 2 wanted: softwood 20 mm × 50 mm × length ($\frac{3}{4}$″ × 2″ × length)
C. Chair Stops, 8 wanted: battens 25 mm × 25 mm × 75 mm (1″ × 1″ × 3″)

Shopping List for Heavy Armchairs
A. Base: softwood 20 mm ($\frac{3}{4}$″) × width of chair plus 75 mm (3″) × length of chair plus 255 mm (10″) for foot rest plus 75 mm (3″)
B. Cross Timbers: softwood 20 mm × 150 mm × width of chair ($\frac{3}{4}$″ × 6″ × width of chair)
C. Chair Stops, 8 wanted: battens 25 mm × 25 mm × 75 mm (1″ × 1″ × 3″)

Instructions for Light Armchairs
1. Fix strengthening strips B to base A (see illustration).
2. Fix castors.
3. Glasspaper and paint.

Instructions for Heavy Armchairs

1. Make base A with softwood planks (see illustration).
2. Fix castors.
3. Put chair on trolley and mark out where feet battens have to be fixed.
4. Fix feet battens.
5. Glasspaper and paint.

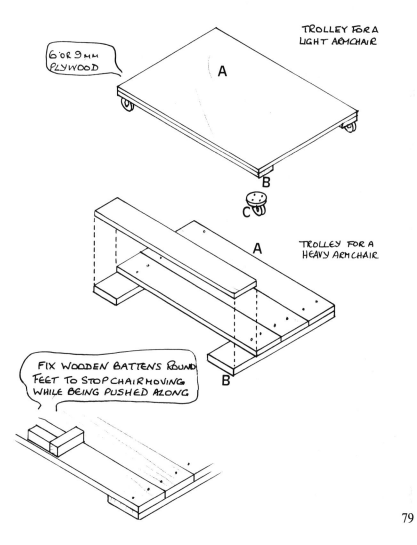

TROLLEY FOR A LIGHT ARMCHAIR

6 OR 9 MM PLYWOOD

A

B

C

TROLLEY FOR A HEAVY ARMCHAIR

A

FIX WOODEN BATTENS ROUND FEET TO STOP CHAIR MOVING WHILE BEING PUSHED ALONG

B

TROLLEY TABLE

This table is of similar construction to others in this book, but to stop it slipping off, two little wooden dowels peg it to the trolley. A range of holes is drilled, so that the table can be placed either closer to you or further away.

The height and width will depend on the size of the chair and the person sitting in it, and this you must find out yourself. Try and make your armchair a real living centre and have several tables all fitted out for various activities.

Shopping List
A. Tray: plywood 9 mm × 360 mm (14″)
B. Sides, 2 wanted: plywood 9 mm × 300 mm (12″)
C. Side Battens, 2 wanted: softwood 40 mm × 40 mm × 300 mm ($1\frac{1}{2}$″ × $1\frac{1}{2}$″ × 12″)
D. Front: plywood 9 mm × 100 mm (4″). The front must not restrict leg movement but must be as deep as possible to give sides maximum strength
E. Front Battens, 2 wanted: softwood 40 mm × 40 mm × 100mm ($1\frac{1}{2}$″ × $1\frac{1}{2}$″ × 4″)
F. Dowels, 4 wanted: wooden dowel 4 mm diameter ($\frac{1}{4}$″) × 25 mm (1″) long

Instructions
1. Carefully work out all the dimensions for the table.
2. Fix side battens C to sides B 40 mm ($1\frac{1}{2}$″) in from edge (see illustration).
3. Fix front battens E to front D.
4. Drill holes in bottom of sides B for dowels F, 12 mm ($\frac{1}{2}$″) from each end.
5. Glue in dowels F (see illustration).
6. Fix sides B to front D.

7. Fix top A to assembled sides B and front D.
8. Glasspaper and paint or stain.

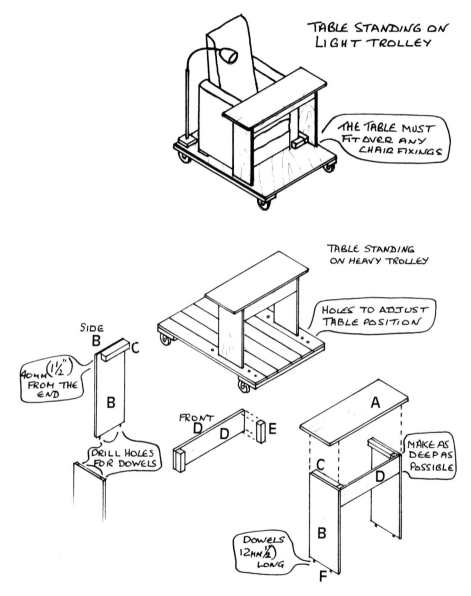

TABLE STANDING ON LIGHT TROLLEY

THE TABLE MUST FIT OVER ANY CHAIR FIXINGS

TABLE STANDING ON HEAVY TROLLEY

HOLES TO ADJUST TABLE POSITION

SIDE
B C
B

40mm (1½") FROM THE END

DRILL HOLES FOR DOWELS

FRONT
D D E

A
C D

MAKE AS DEEP AS POSSIBLE

DOWELS 12mm (½") LONG

B

F

TILTING THE ARMCHAIR

Your medical adviser may prefer you to sit in a chair which is at a slight angle. This can be done by making small angled blocks as illustrated. With the chair tilted back, your feet will be further away from the ground and a foot rest may be needed to let you sit comfortably.

Shopping List
A.   Blocks: plywood or wood off-cuts about
      100 mm × 100 mm × height (4″ × 4″) to give required angle.

Construction: Glue and Screw

Instructions
1.   Glue pieces of wood together to make blocks A.
2.   Remove castors.
3.   Cut the glued wood to shape and angle for blocks A.
4.   Fix blocks A to front feet of chair.
5.   Check for stability and, if the chair seems likely to tip back under normal use, make a stabilising board as illustrated.
6.   Glasspaper and paint or stain.

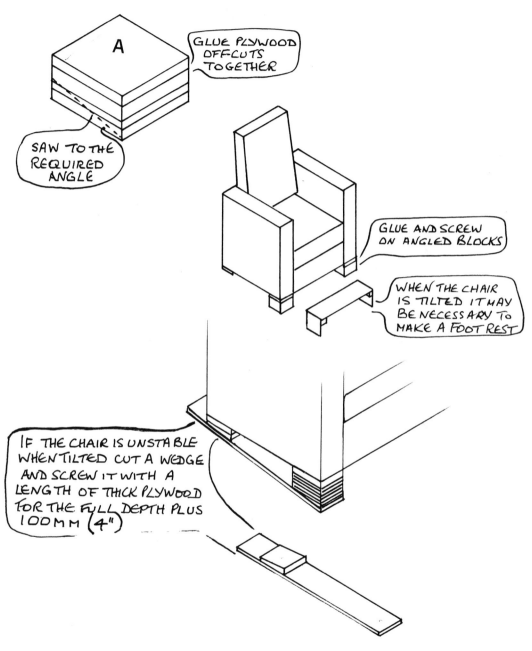

GLUE PLYWOOD
OFFCUTS
TOGETHER

A

SAW TO THE
REQUIRED
ANGLE

GLUE AND SCREW
ON ANGLED BLOCKS

WHEN THE CHAIR
IS TILTED IT MAY
BE NECESSARY TO
MAKE A FOOT REST

IF THE CHAIR IS UNSTABLE
WHEN TILTED CUT A WEDGE
AND SCREW IT WITH A
LENGTH OF THICK PLYWOOD
FOR THE FULL DEPTH PLUS
100MM (4")

ANGLED FOOT REST

When reclining in an armchair an angled foot rest can be much more comfortable and relaxing than a flat one. It should be well padded, particularly where the heels rest. In cold weather a small blanket wrapped round the feet will keep them nice and warm in their little box. Work out the angles by resting the person's feet on cushions. The sizes given in the shopping list are only intended as a guide, because the size of the feet play a big part in the size of the finished foot rest.

Shopping List

A. Sides, 2 wanted: plywood 9 mm × 200 mm × 300 mm
    (8″ × 12″)
B. Ends, 2 wanted: plywood 9 mm × 200 mm × 200 mm (8″ × 8″)
C. Battens: softwood 25 mm × 25 mm × 150 mm (1″ × 1″ × 6″)

Construction: Glue and Nail

Instructions

1. Mark out angles on ends B as illustrated.
2. Fix battens C to sides A.
3. Fix ends B to sides A.

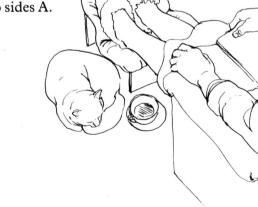

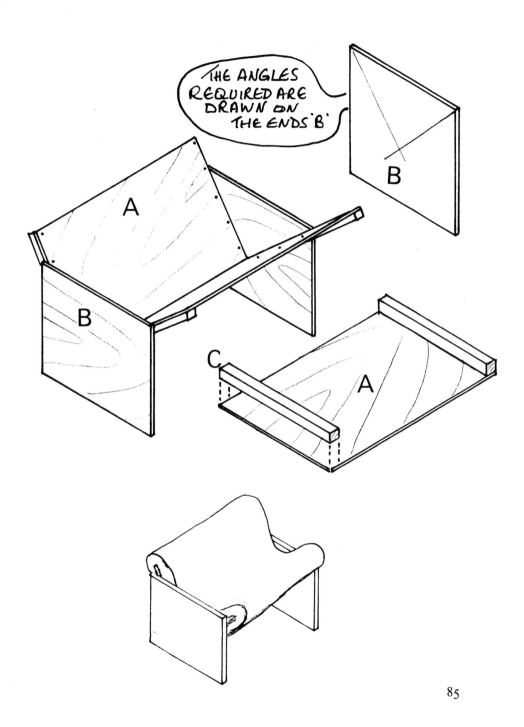

85

BOOK REST

A book rest can be made to fit any armchair or bed table, whatever its size. To hold a heavy book soon tires the strongest of us, so a book rest is a must for the avid reader.

To obtain the preferred angle, measure it while the person is reading a book.

Shopping List
A. Board: plywood 4 mm × 250 mm × 300 mm (10″ × 12″)
B. Angle Brackets, 2 wanted: softwood 12 mm × 150 mm × 200 mm ($\frac{1}{2}$″ × 6″ × 8″)
C. Rest: softwood 12 mm × 30 mm × 300 mm ($\frac{1}{2}$″ × $1\frac{1}{4}$″ × 12″)

Construction: Glue and Nail

Instructions
1. Find the preferred angle.
2. Cut angle brackets B as illustrated.
3. Fix angle brackets to board A.
4. Fix rest C 12 mm ($\frac{1}{2}$″) from the bottom.
5. Glasspaper and paint.

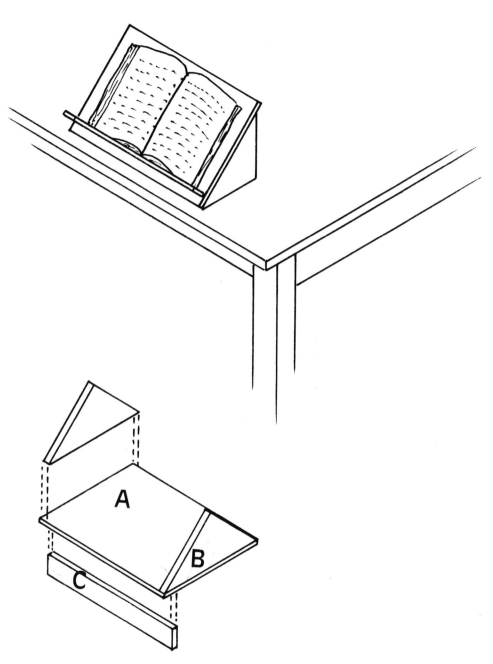

A

B

C

ADJUSTABLE BOOK REST

This is almost as easy to make as the fixed version—apart from the fact that a book can be held at almost any angle, it has the advantage that it will fold flat for travelling.

Shopping List

A.   Board: plywood 4 mm × 250 mm × 300 mm (10″ × 12″)

B.   Board Side, 2 wanted: softwood 12 mm × 30 mm × 250 mm ($\frac{1}{2}$″ × $1\frac{1}{4}$″ × 10″)

C.   Legs, 2 wanted: softwood 12 mm × 30 mm × 250 mm ($\frac{1}{2}$″ × $1\frac{1}{4}$″ × 10″)

D.   Rest: softwood 12 mm × 30 mm × 300 mm ($\frac{1}{2}$″ × $1\frac{1}{4}$″ × 12″)

E.   Wing Nut and Bolt, 2 wanted: about 3 mm diameter × 37 mm long ($\frac{1}{4}$″ diameter × $1\frac{1}{2}$″)

Construction: Glue and Nail

Instructions

1.   Drill holes in sides B and legs C for wing nuts and bolts E.
2.   Cut off corners of sides B as illustrated.
3.   Fix sides B to board A.
4.   Fix rest D to board A 25 m (1″) from the bottom.
5.   Glasspaper all parts and paint.
6.   Fit legs C to sides B with screws and wing nuts.

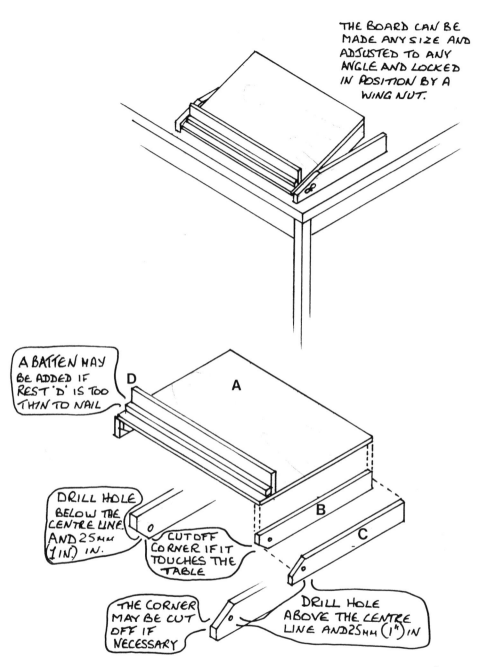

THE BOARD CAN BE MADE ANY SIZE AND ADJUSTED TO ANY ANGLE AND LOCKED IN POSITION BY A WING NUT.

A BATTEN MAY BE ADDED IF REST 'D' IS TOO THIN TO NAIL

D

A

DRILL HOLE BELOW THE CENTRE LINE AND 25mm (1 IN.) IN.

CUT OFF CORNER IF IT TOUCHES THE TABLE

B

C

THE CORNER MAY BE CUT OFF IF NECESSARY

DRILL HOLE ABOVE THE CENTRE LINE AND 25mm (1") IN

89

BEDROOM

Reading in bed and having to get up during the night mean that good lighting and an easily reached switch are musts. Various little modifications to furniture are described in the following pages, and these should only be done with your medical adviser's approval.

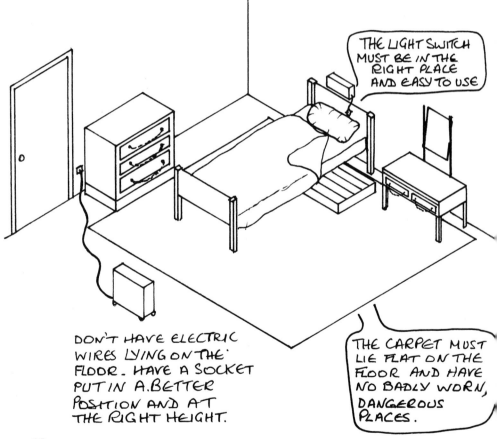

CHEST OF DRAWERS

The drawers in some old chests are heavy. If they do not open easily, have them attended to before thinking about any changes. Should you feel that changing the knobs will be of no help, tie a piece of soft rope between them. This will let you pull the drawer open with your hands at their most comfortable distance apart and if you need to use only one hand the drawer will open smoothly if the centre of the rope is pulled.

Shopping List
A.   Length of soft rope. When finding this measurement, don't forget to allow for the knot.

Instructions
1.   Tie the rope between the knobs but do not stretch it too tightly as it will then be too close to the drawer and hard to grasp.

PLINTH FOR A CHEST OF DRAWERS

Some of the older chests of drawers are very heavy and would need a strong plinth, while the newer ones, often made of plywood and other man-made materials, can safely be placed on a much lighter structure. All these chests, whether heavy or light, can become unstable if an open drawer filled with clothes is leant on. To overcome this problem fix the chest to the wall with a little bracket as illustrated.

Shopping List
A.   Sides Long, 2 wanted: 12 mm ($\frac{1}{2}''$) × height required × length of chest + 50 mm (2″)

B.   Sides Short, 2 wanted: softwood 12 mm ($\frac{1}{2}''$) × height required × depth of chest + 50 mm (2″)

C.   Top: softwood 12 mm ($\frac{1}{2}''$) × depth of chest + 50 mm (2″) × length of chest + 50 mm (2″)

D.   Top Corner Battens, 4 wanted: softwood 25 mm × 25 mm × 75 mm (1″ × 1″ × 3″)

Construction: Glue and Screw

Instructions
1.   Fix sides A to sides B.
2.   Fix top planks C to assembled sides A and B. For heavy chests, fix corner battens D.
3.   Glasspaper and paint to match chest.
4.   Fix plinth to wall with metal brackets.
5.   Place chest on plinth and fix chest to the wall with metal brackets.

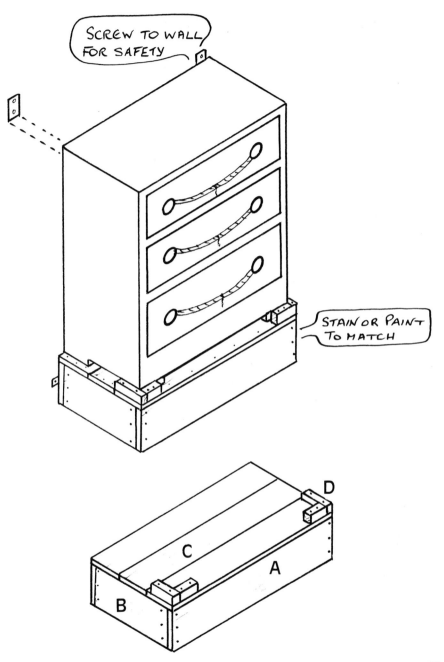

DRESSING TABLE DRAWER PULL

Dressing table drawers are not usually heavy but can be difficult to open by the knob, particularly if you also have a problem in getting your fingers round it. Two simple solutions are given which only take a few minutes to make. The rope does not have to be a piece cut off the clothes line; look for some colourful artificial silk rope, sometimes used for curtains. It comes in many colours and one may be found to match the room's décor.

Shopping List for First Solution
A.   Length of rope or thick cord
B.   2 Eye screws

Second Solution
A.   Length of rope or thick cord
B.   Length of 25 mm (1″) diameter dowel

Instructions
See illustrations.

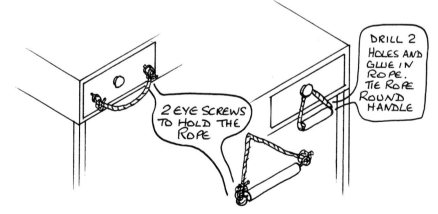

WARDROBE

This is often a heavy piece of furniture with doors which are difficult to open and close. Get a man in to make all the adjustments that you need and at the same time he can do any other alterations to it which will make life easier for you. If it has now become a problem to reach up to get clothes off the rail, have it lowered, but before doing this try a long handled reacher as illustrated. If ladies do not like hanging their dresses over a low rail a long reacher has to be used. Heavy items such as overcoats and rainwear should be kept by the front door where they can dry without making other clothing damp.

Modern glues make it possible to fix all sorts of wooden, metal and plastic fittings to the inside of the door, and these can be placed where you can easily reach them. Various hooks, rails and shelves are available in all sorts of sizes in the shops.

Shopping List
Door Hooks
A. Board: softwood 12 mm ($\frac{1}{2}$″) × 50 mm (2″) × measure door for this dimension
B. Hooks: a wide range of shapes and sizes is available

Door Rail
A. Board: softwood 12 mm ($\frac{1}{2}$″) × 50 mm (2″) × measure the door for this dimension
B. Sides, 2 wanted: softwood 12 mm × 50 mm × 75 mm ($\frac{1}{2}$″ × 2″ × 3″)
C. Rail: wooden dowel 12 mm ($\frac{1}{2}$″) diameter × length to suit

Clothes Rail
A. Ends, 2 wanted: softwood 12 mm × 50 mm × 75 mm ($\frac{1}{2}$″ × 2″ × 3″)
B. Rail: wooden dowel about 25 mm (1″) diameter × length to suit

Long Reacher
A. Handle: wooden dowel about a metre (36″) long
B. Hook: one very large hook which can be bent to shape

Instructions for Door Hooks
1. Mark out for hooks and screw holes if required.
2. Drill holes and fix screws.
3. Finish by glasspapering and painting or staining.

Instructions for Door Rail
1. Drill sides B for rail C.
2. Fix sides B to board A.
3. Fix rail C to sides B with glue.
4. Finish by glasspapering and painting or staining.

Instructions for Clothes Rail
1. Mark out ends A for rail and screws if required.
2. Drill holes.
3. Fix rail B into ends A with glue.
4. Finish by glasspapering and painting or staining.

Instructions for Long Reacher
1. Drill pilot hole for hook half the diameter of the screw.
2. Bend screw roughly to shape.
3. Fit screw into handle.
    Remove the hook from the handle for any reshaping.

96

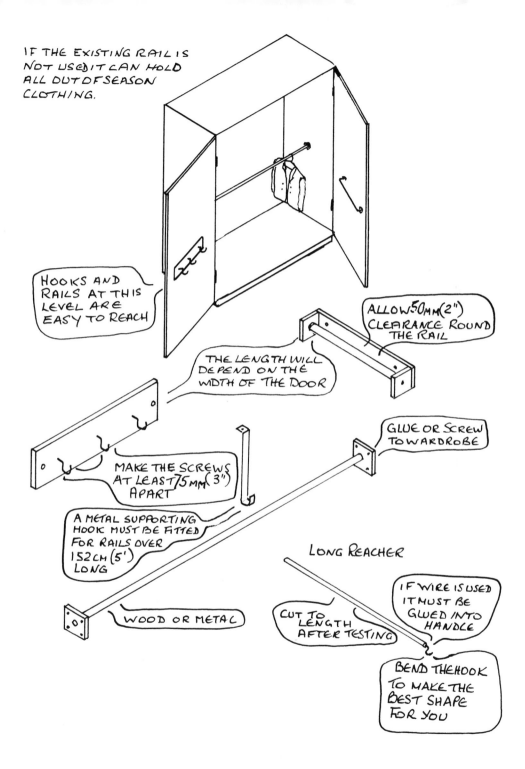

BEDSIDE STEP

A bedside step effectively reduces the height your bed is from the ground. By first stepping on to the box you should feel much safer and therefore more confident about getting into and out of bed. Get medical advice on the height and size to make the step. It is not possible to give dimensions but the illustrations should be studied.

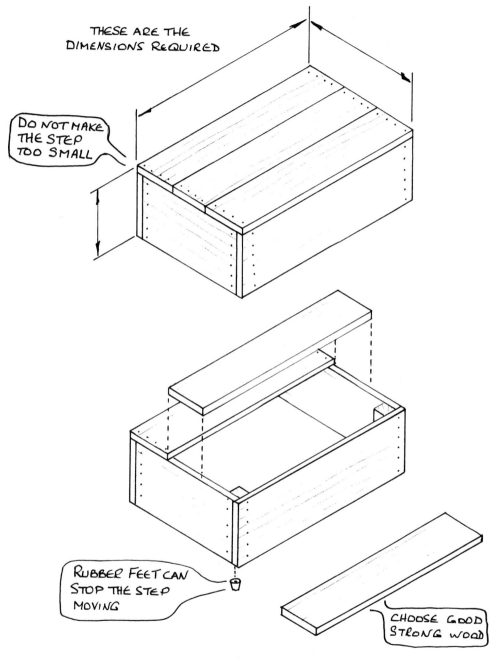

BED CLOTHES SUPPORT

Some discomfort may be felt by the pressure of the bed clothes on the feet, particularly when lying on the back with the toes pressing against well tucked-in sheets and blankets. This little support holds up the bed clothes to give the feet freedom from this pressure. See the illustration as to how it is placed in the bed. Guide dimensions only are given as the thickness of the mattress may make it necessary to increase the height of the back.

Shopping List
A.   Back, plywood 9 mm × 460 mm × 510 mm high (18″ × 20″ high)
B.   Top and Base, one of each: plywood 9 mm × 250 mm × 460 mm (10″ × 18″)
C.   Battens, 2 wanted: softwood 40 mm × 40 mm × 460 mm ($1\frac{1}{2}″ × 1\frac{1}{2}″ × 18″$)

Construction: Glue and Nail

Instructions
1. Cut off corners as illustrated and glasspaper all sharp edges so that they will not damage the bed clothes. It is better to round the corners.
2. Fix battens C to back A.
3. Fix base and top B to back A.
4. Thoroughly glasspaper.
5. Finish by painting.

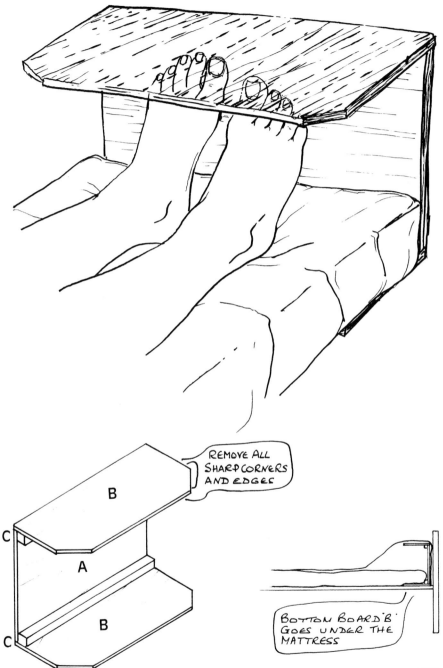

REMOVE ALL SHARP CORNERS AND EDGES

B

C

A

B

C

BOTTOM BOARD "B" GOES UNDER THE MATTRESS

BEDSIDE CABINET

The bedside cabinet can be given a few little modifications to make it an even more useful piece of furniture. The illustration gives a number of these which will not take up much time or cost much money. Usually, removing the door and raising the cabinet up on a plinth are enough.

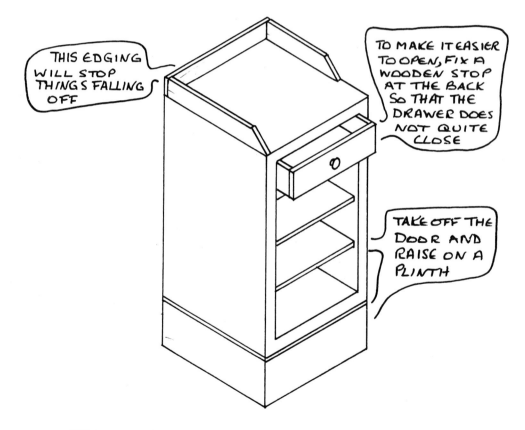

BED LIGHT

It is very important that a light can be switched on and off by just reaching out for a switch. There can be nothing more frightening than to wake up in the middle of the night and not be able to put the light on. If there is already a light fitted over the bed it must be altered to make it easy to use, and an example of this is illustrated. An electrician can do this because he has the choice of many types of light and switch which are safe and easy to fit.

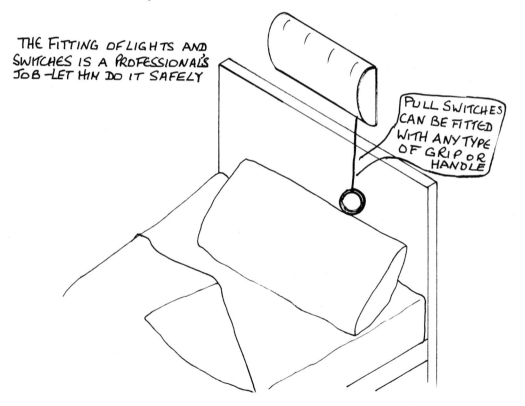

THE FITTING OF LIGHTS AND SWITCHES IS A PROFESSIONAL'S JOB – LET HIM DO IT SAFELY

PULL SWITCHES CAN BE FITTED WITH ANY TYPE OF GRIP OR HANDLE

THERE ARE MANY KINDS OF SWITCHES ON THE MARKET. LOOK FOR ONE WHICH BEST SUITS YOU.

BED TRAY

Being comfortable while sitting up in bed for any length of time is not an easy thing to achieve, but with a well-designed back rest and a bed tray which is the right size and height, it is possible to overcome at least some of the problems. If, after searching the shops, the right one cannot be found, the tray illustrated here is easy to make and will not cost very much. Do not hesitate to change any of the dimensions as this is the only way to get the most suitable bed tray for you.

Shopping List
A. Tray: plywood 6 mm × 250 mm × 760 mm (10″ × 30″)
B. Sides, 2 wanted: plywood 6 mm × 250 mm × 300 mm (10″ × 12″)
C. Front Edge: softwood 10 mm × 25 mm × 740 mm ($\frac{3}{8}$″ × 1″ × 29$\frac{1}{4}$″)
D. Side Edge, 2 wanted: softwood 10 mm × 25 mm × 250 mm ($\frac{3}{8}$″ × 1″ × 10″)
E. Batten, 2 wanted: softwood 30 mm × 30 mm × 250 mm (1$\frac{1}{4}$″ × 1$\frac{1}{4}$″ × 10″)

Construction: Glue and Nail

Instructions
1. Cut sides B as illustrated and well round the corners.
2. Fix battens E to sides B.
3. Fix sides B to tray A 40 mm (1$\frac{1}{2}$″) from each end.
4. Cut the corners off side edges D.
5. Fix edge C and edges D to tray A.
6. Glasspaper thoroughly so that no damage can be done to bed clothes.
7. Finish by painting.

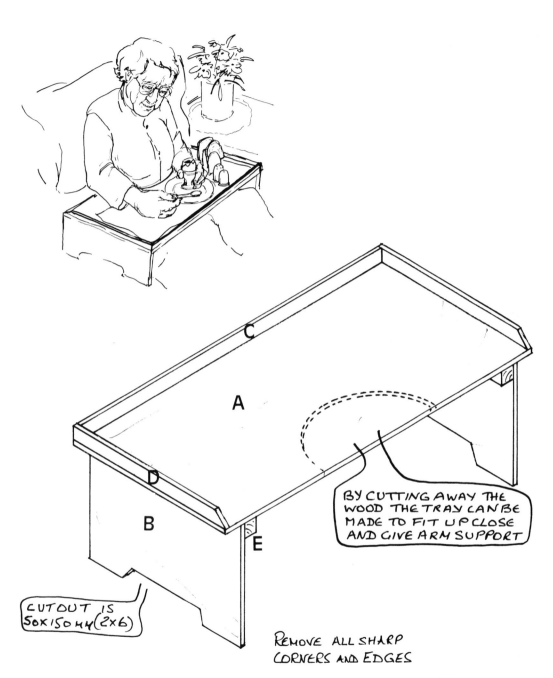

C

A

D

B

E

BY CUTTING AWAY THE WOOD THE TRAY CAN BE MADE TO FIT UP CLOSE AND GIVE ARM SUPPORT

CUTOUT IS 50×150MM (2×6)

REMOVE ALL SHARP CORNERS AND EDGES

105

BED TABLE FOR HOBBIES

This bed table is extra wide and extra strong and, although heavy, it does give a firm working surface to those who would like to occupy themselves with some hobby. For some people, a cut-out may have to be made in the table as this will allow it to fit close to the body and give some support to the arms; this is shown on the drawing with a dotted line.

It is not possible to give all the dimensions as some of them depend on the height of the bed and the height of the table top in relation to the person in a sitting position in the bed. It is easy to get these dimensions by measuring the person in exactly the way he or she would work.

Shopping List
A. Table: plywood 9 mm × 400 mm × 600 mm (16″ × 24″)
B. Table Edge Long: softwood 12 mm × 50 mm × 600 mm
    ($\frac{1}{2}$″ × 2″ × 24″)
C. Table Edge Short: softwood 12 mm × 50 mm × 200 mm
    ($\frac{1}{2}$″ × 2″ × 8″)
D. Back: plywood 9 mm × 400 mm × 760 mm* (16″ × 30″*)
E. Back Bracket Short, 2 wanted: softwood
    25 mm × 25 mm × 350 mm (1″ × 1″ × 13$\frac{3}{4}$″)
F. Back Bracket Long, 2 wanted: softwood
    25 mm × 25 mm × 760 mm* (1″ × 1″ × 30″*)
G. Side, 2 wanted: plywood 9 mm × 200 mm × 760 mm* (8″ × 30″*)
H. Side Battens, 4 wanted: softwood 25 mm × 25 mm × 150 mm
    (1″ × 1″ × 6″)
I. Base: plywood 9 mm × 400 mm × 760 mm (16″ × 30″)
J. Skids, 2 wanted: softwood 25 mm × 40 mm × 760 mm
    (1″ × 1″ × 30″)

★These dimensions must be measured by you.

Construction: Glue and Nail

Instructions

1. Make the assemblies A, D, G and I as illustrated (overleaf).
2. Fix sides G to back D.
3. Round the ends of skids J as illustrated.
4. Fix base I to complete back assembly.
5. Fix table to complete back assembly.
6. Finish by glasspapering and painting.

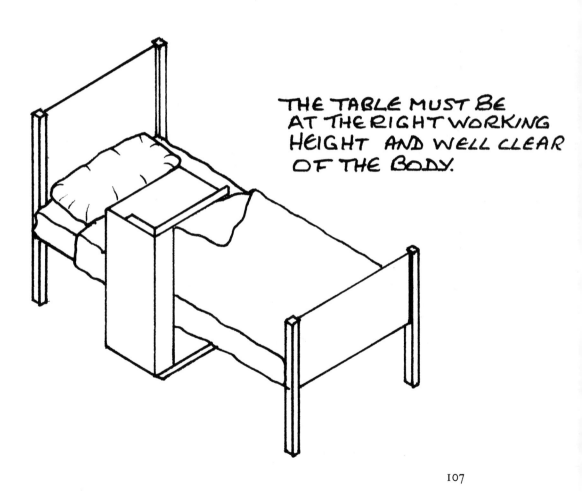

THE TABLE MUST BE
AT THE RIGHT WORKING
HEIGHT AND WELL CLEAR
OF THE BODY.

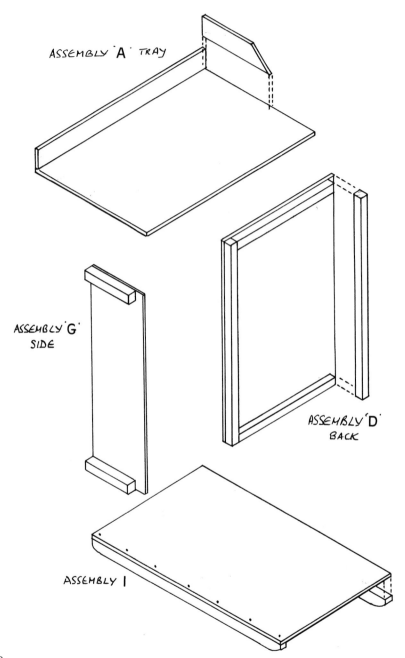

ASSEMBLY 'A' TRAY

ASSEMBLY 'G'
SIDE

ASSEMBLY 'D'
BACK

ASSEMBLY I

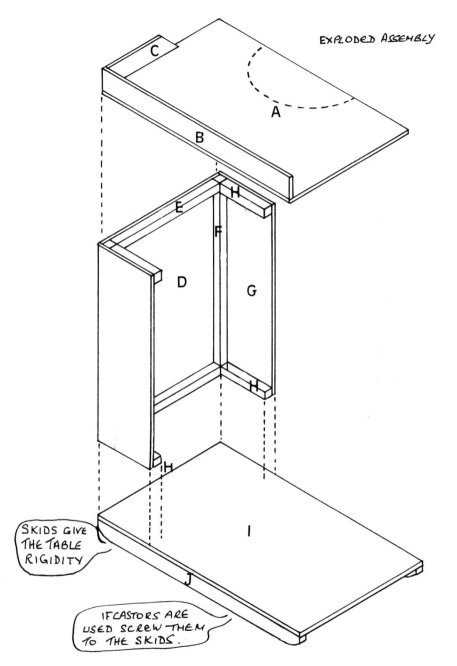

EXPLODED ASSEMBLY

C

A

B

E

H

F

D

G

H

H

SKIDS GIVE
THE TABLE
RIGIDITY

I

J

IF CASTORS ARE
USED SCREW THEM
TO THE SKIDS.

IRONING BOARD BED TABLE

Not all ironing boards can be used for this purpose and some beds are too low, but you may be lucky and find this idea a quick and easy way of providing a bed table, although only as a temporary measure. Usually, the only ironing boards which are suitable are those of a wide modern design as they are more stable. Besides going over the bed, they can be placed alongside it to make a long bed table, and when not needed can be folded up and put away.

If you do not want to make a tray, an ordinary one can be used.

Shopping List for a Tray
A.   Base: plywood 6 mm × 250 mm × 350 mm (10″ × 14″)
B.   Top Edge: softwood 10 mm × 50 mm × 350 mm ($\frac{3}{8}$″ × 2″ × 14″)
C.   Sides, 2 wanted: softwood 10 mm × 50 mm × 190 mm ($\frac{3}{8}$″ × 2″ × 7$\frac{1}{2}$″)

Construction: Glue and Nail

Instructions
1. Fix top edge B to base A.
2. Fix sides C to base A.
3. Finish by glasspapering and painting.

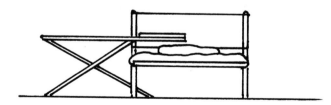

THE IRONING BOARD
MUST GO OVER THE BED
FAR ENOUGH. TRY IT
AT VARIOUS HEIGHTS.

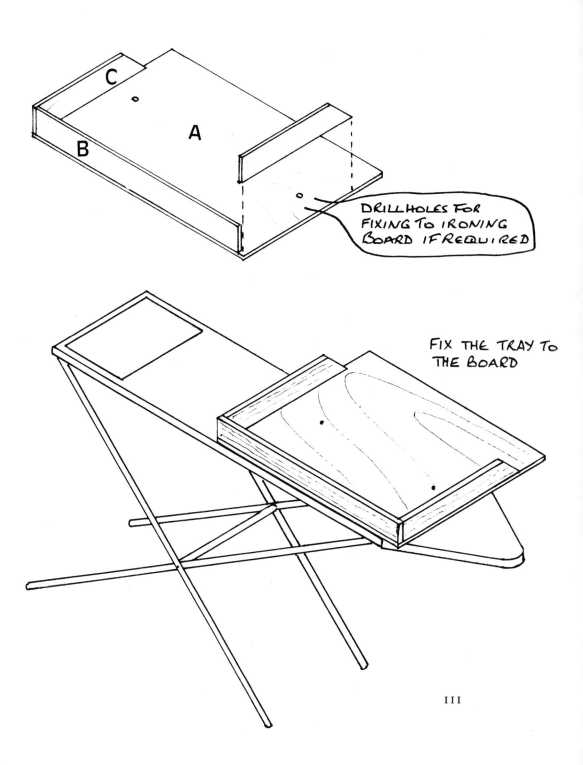

DRILL HOLES FOR FIXING TO IRONING BOARD IF REQUIRED

FIX THE TRAY TO THE BOARD

BED RAISERS

Three ways are given on how to make a bed higher. By having this done, the task of others helping you will be made easier and not nearly so back-breaking. If you are having physiotherapy treatment, care must be taken to ensure that the bed is still strong enough to take the extra strain of the exercises.

Bed Raiser for Metal Bed Frames
As it is difficult to drill and fix wood or metal to a metal-framed bed, it is easier to place the legs in small wooden boxes as illustrated. This method can, of course, be used on all types of bed and is particularly suitable if a bed has to be put back to its original height.

Shopping List for Four Raisers
A. Base, 4 wanted: plywood 9 mm × 90 mm × 90 mm ($3\frac{1}{2}'' × 3\frac{1}{2}''$)
B. Sides Small, 8 wanted: plywood 9 mm × 72 mm × 150 mm ($2\frac{13}{16}'' × 6''$)
C. Sides Large, 8 wanted: plywood 9 mm × 90 mm × 150 mm ($3\frac{1}{2}'' × 6''$)
D. Blocks, 4 wanted: softwood to fit into box × height required
E. Countersunk wood screws: No 8 × 25 mm ($1''$) × 96

Construction: Glue and Screw

Instructions
1. Drill and countersink holes for base A and sides C.
2. Drill pilot holes for screws in sides B half the diameter of the screws.
3. Fix sides B to sides C.
4. Fix assembled sides B and C to base A.
5. Glasspaper and stain or paint to match bed.
6. Cut blocks to size and fit into boxes.

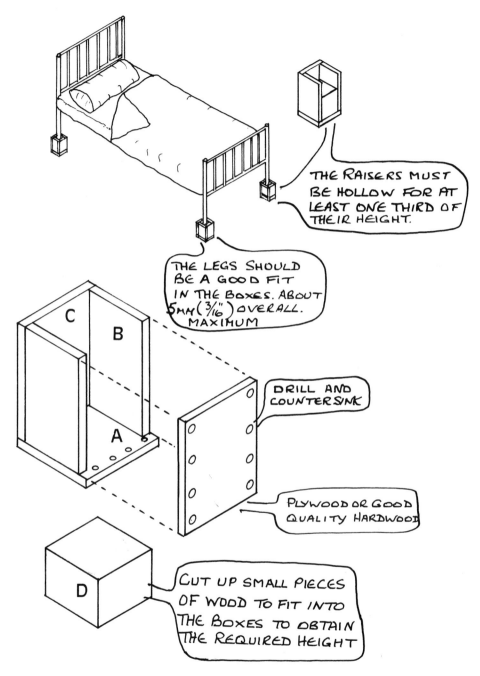

THE RAISERS MUST BE HOLLOW FOR AT LEAST ONE THIRD OF THEIR HEIGHT.

THE LEGS SHOULD BE A GOOD FIT IN THE BOXES. ABOUT 5MM ($\frac{3}{16}$") OVERALL. MAXIMUM

C
B
A

DRILL AND COUNTERSINK

PLYWOOD OR GOOD QUALITY HARDWOOD

D

CUT UP SMALL PIECES OF WOOD TO FIT INTO THE BOXES TO OBTAIN THE REQUIRED HEIGHT

Wooden Bed Raiser for Wooden Framed Beds
This is a quick and effective way of raising a bed but care must be taken in choosing the wood. It must be well seasoned and not liable to split under the weight of the bed and the person in it. Off-cuts of plywood laminated together with a good glue give excellent results.

Shopping List
A. Four pieces of well seasoned wood about the size of the bed leg. The length is calculated by adding the height the bed has to be raised plus at least 150 mm (6″)
B. Nuts and bolts about 5 mm ($\frac{3}{16}$″)diameter, 8 wanted
C. Washers for above. These should be as large a diameter as possible to avoid splitting the wood when the nuts are tightened.

Instructions
1. Drill bed legs and extensions A to suit bolts.
2. Bolt extensions to bed legs.
3. Stain or paint to match the bed.

NUTS AND BOLTS
OR
NUTS AND SCREWS
WITH A WASHER
BOTH SIDES

PLYWOOD
LAMINATED
LEG

Metal Raiser for Wooden Bed Frames

Angle iron or angle aluminium makes a very strong leg and is quick to fit.

Shopping List

A. Four pieces of angle iron or angle aluminium. The length is calculated in the same way as the wooden extension
B. Nuts and bolts about 5 mm ($\frac{3}{16}$″) diameter, 16 wanted
C. Washers, large, 32 wanted

Instructions

1. Round all corners and edges of extenders A.
2. Drill bed legs and extenders A to suit nuts. Stagger the holes.
3. Bolt extenders to the bed.
4. Paint to match bed.

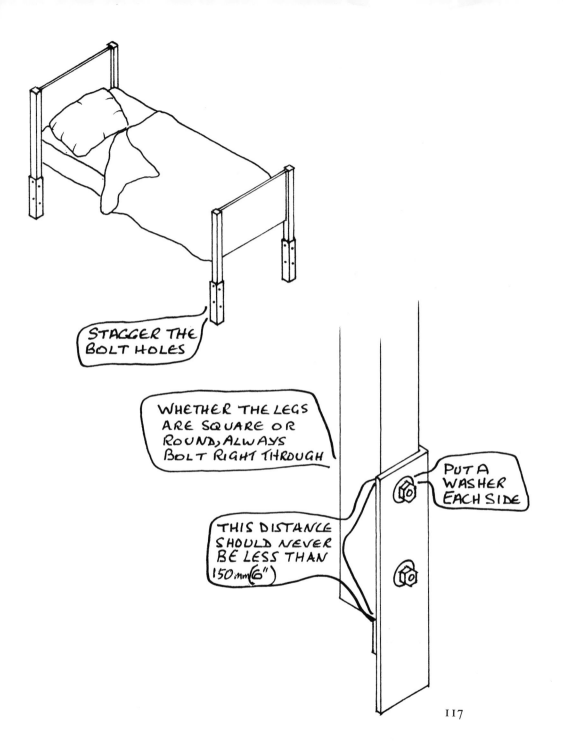

OVER THE BED TABLE

This table can be made by a skilled DIY man if he has a good workshop and the right tools. It must be well made as it is a general purpose table and ideal for all hobbies or even making things for sale. There is no reason why it cannot be fitted out as a work bench with vice, electric sockets and lighting.

To work out all the wood sizes, it is necessary to know the width of the bed and the height the table top has to be from the floor.

Shopping List

A. Table Top: plywood 9 mm × 400 mm × length (16″ × length)
B. Back Edge: softwood 10 mm × 50 mm × length ($\frac{3}{8}$″ × 2″ × length)
C. Side Edge, 2 wanted: softwood 10 mm × 50 mm × 390 mm ($\frac{3}{8}$″ × 2″ × 15$\frac{7}{8}$″)
D. Legs, 4 wanted: softwood 10 mm × 45 mm × 45 mm height ($\frac{3}{8}$″ × 1$\frac{3}{4}$″ × 1$\frac{3}{4}$″ × height)
E. Leg Ties Long, 2 wanted: softwood 12 mm × 75 mm × length ($\frac{1}{2}$″ × 3″ × length)
F. Leg Ties Short, 2 wanted: softwood 12 mm × 75 mm × 310 mm ($\frac{1}{2}$″ × 3″ × 12″)
G. Lower Leg Ties 2, wanted: softwood 12 mm × 75 mm × 310 mm ($\frac{1}{2}$″ × 3″ × 12″)

No instructions are given as a skilled person would know how to make all the joints.

Note. In order to find the correct measurements for the table top, back edge, legs and long leg ties, calculate the length from the width of the bed and the height when the person is in bed.

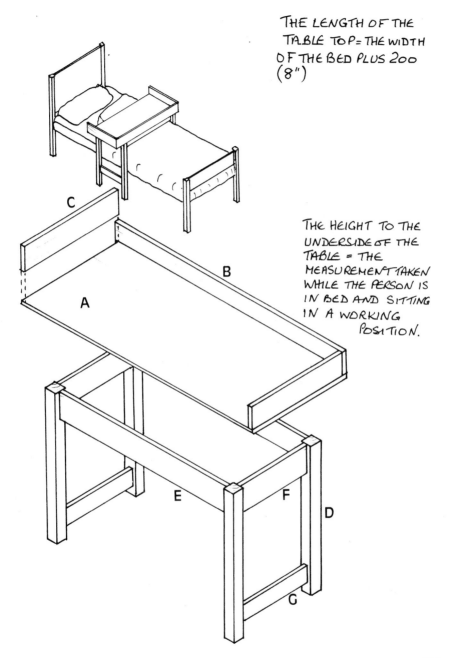

THE LENGTH OF THE TABLE TOP = THE WIDTH OF THE BED PLUS 200 (8")

THE HEIGHT TO THE UNDERSIDE OF THE TABLE = THE MEASUREMENT TAKEN WHILE THE PERSON IS IN BED AND SITTING IN A WORKING POSITION.

C

B

A

E

F

D

G

BATHROOM AND LAVATORY

For an elderly person, the bathroom can be one of the most hazardous rooms in the house. The ideas suggested here will provide support where it is needed most – in getting in and out of the bath and in using the lavatory. Handrails fixed at strategic points can also make it easier to move about the room.

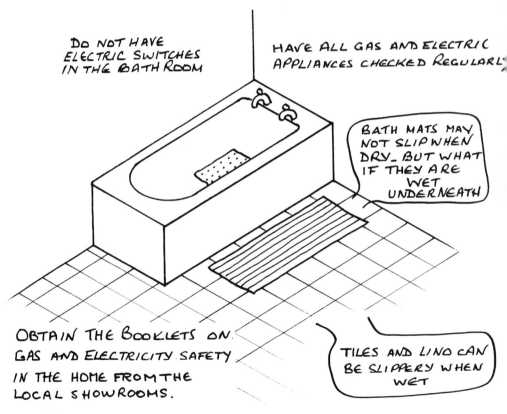

DO NOT HAVE ELECTRIC SWITCHES IN THE BATH ROOM

HAVE ALL GAS AND ELECTRIC APPLIANCES CHECKED REGULARLY

BATH MATS MAY NOT SLIP WHEN DRY. BUT WHAT IF THEY ARE WET UNDERNEATH

OBTAIN THE BOOKLETS ON GAS AND ELECTRICITY SAFETY IN THE HOME FROM THE LOCAL SHOWROOMS.

TILES AND LINO CAN BE SLIPPERY WHEN WET

120

SAFE BATH PLUG

By using a length of plastic tube instead of a plug, the water can never get too deep because once the level reaches the top of the tube it runs away. For example, a 150 mm (6″) length of tube will only allow the water to become about 140 mm (5½″) deep. A smaller diameter pipe can be made to be a good push fit by winding plastic insulation around it.

A gentle push with the toe is usually enough to make the tube come out of the hole when you have finished bathing, but a length of cord or light chain can be fixed to the top of the tube so that it can be pulled out by hand.

Shopping List
A.   Plug Tube: semi rigid plastic such as polythene
B.   Plastic Insulation Tape

Instructions
1. Fit tube into plug hole by winding on insulation tape until a good push fit is achieved.

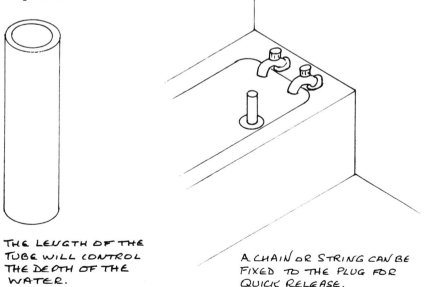

THE LENGTH OF THE
TUBE WILL CONTROL
THE DEPTH OF THE
WATER.

A CHAIN OR STRING CAN BE
FIXED TO THE PLUG FOR
QUICK RELEASE.

BATH SEAT

If you use a wheelchair this extended bath seat will help you to get from your chair to sit over the bath and back into the chair again. Some baths are made of plastic and tend to bend under pressure, making the fit of a seat important.

    If you are able to get down into the bath but need a low seat, it is better to buy one, particularly if the bath is made of plastic.

Shopping List
A.   Side: softwood 20 mm × 255 mm × height from floor to top edge of bath ($\frac{3}{4}'' \times 10''$)

B.   Seat: softwood 20 mm × 255 mm ($\frac{3}{4}'' \times 10''$) × measurement from wall to outside edge of bath plus length of seat (usually about 255 mm (10''))

C.   Brackets, 2 wanted: plywood 9 mm × 150 mm × 150 mm (6'' × 6'') cut diagonally into 2

D.   Batten Short, 2 wanted: softwood 25 mm × 25 mm × 125 mm (1'' × 1'' × 5'')

E.   Batten Long, 2 wanted: softwood 25 mm × 25 mm × 150 mm (1'' × 1'' × 6'')

F.   Side Batten: softwood 25 mm × 25 mm × 200 mm (1'' × 1'' × 8'')

G.   Bath Block: softwood 50 mm × 50 mm × 225 mm (2'' × 2'' × 10'')

H.   Dowels, 2 wanted: 5 mm diameter × 100 mm ($\frac{1}{4}''$ diameter × 4'')

I.   Wall Bracket: softwood 20 mm × 75 mm × 355 mm ($\frac{3}{4}'' \times 3'' \times 14''$)

Construction: Waterproof glue and non rusting screws

Instructions
1. Fix battens D and E to bracket C.
2. Fix batten F to side A.
3. Fix assembled brackets C to side A.
4. Fix assembled side A to seat B.
5. Drill and fix dowels H into bottom of side A.

6. Cut wall bracket I to take seat B.
7. Shape bath block G to fit top of the bath side.
8. Fix wall bracket I to wall.
9. Drill 2 holes in the floor for dowels H about 12 mm ($\frac{1}{2}''$) deep.
10. Place the assembled bath seat in position before fixing the bath block G to seat B, in order to get a good fit.
11. Glasspaper and give several coats of good quality paint.
12. Test thoroughly before use to make sure that it is a strong, rigid structure.

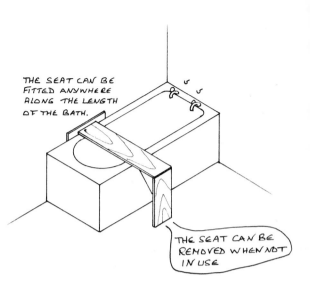

THE SEAT CAN BE FITTED ANYWHERE ALONG THE LENGTH OF THE BATH.

THE SEAT CAN BE REMOVED WHEN NOT IN USE

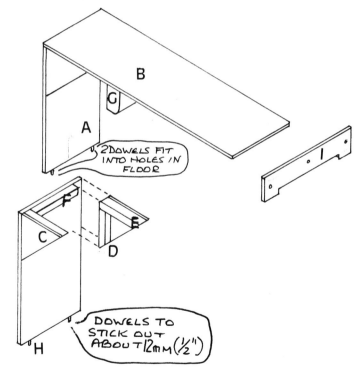

2 DOWELS FIT INTO HOLES IN FLOOR

DOWELS TO STICK OUT ABOUT 12mm ($\frac{1}{2}''$)

BATH LADDER

This little aid may give you just the help you need to move about better in the bath. The rope does not have to be very thick: get advice from a hardwear shop or store, but better still, go to a ships' chandler who supplies the yachtsmen, as he will know how strong various types of rope are. The plastic ones dry quickly, but be careful how the knots are tied as they can slip. The chandler is also the best person to make the ladder. Like all the other bathroom jobs, get a professional to fix the hooks or eyes into the walls and also ask him to supply them, as he will know which are the best ones for this purpose. Your medical adviser must be consulted about the distance between the rungs, as well as on how to use the ladder. If the wall where the hooks have to go is not strong enough, have a board made as illustrated.

Shopping List
A.   Rope: get advice from supplier regarding the thickness. The length required is about $2\frac{1}{2}$ metres ($2\frac{1}{2}$ yards)
B.   Rungs: wooden dowel 30 mm diameter × 300 mm (12″) for each rung required
C.   Hooks, 2 wanted: large with a long threaded screw so that they will go into the wall about 40 mm ($1\frac{1}{2}$″)

Instructions
1.   Cut the rungs to length.
2.   Drill the holes for the rope about 25 mm (1″) from the ends.
3.   Thread and knot rope for rungs.
4.   Tie loops to go over hooks.

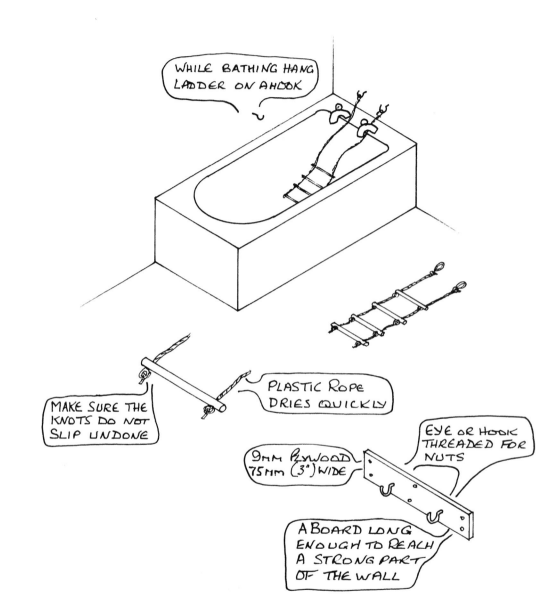

126

TRAPEZE LIFT

Exactly the same remarks apply here as for the Bath Ladder. Shopping list and instructions are also as for the Bath Ladder.

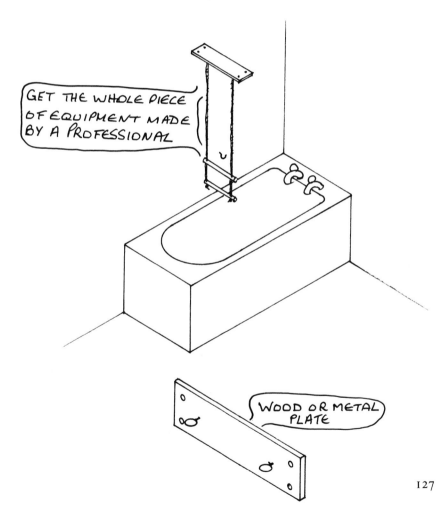

VERTICAL HANDRAIL

The vertical handrail can only be made by a professional and its position in the bathroom decided by the medical adviser. If your hands find it too difficult to hold the strong vertical tube because it is too big, a smaller diameter one can be welded to it and, as illustrated, it need not be vertical. Check that the ceiling and floor are suitable for fixing the plates.

Shopping List
A. Vertical Tube: mild steel 40 mm × height to ceiling ($1\frac{1}{2}''$ × height to ceiling). Test that it will not bend in use
B. Plates, 2 wanted: mild steel 3 mm × 100 mm × 100 mm ($\frac{1}{8}'' \times 4'' \times 4''$)

Instructions
1. Drill plates B for fixing screws.
2. Cut tube A to exact length.
3. Weld tube A to centre plates B.
4. Prepare surface of the metal for painting.
5. Finish with several coats of paint to guard against rust.
6. Fix in position.

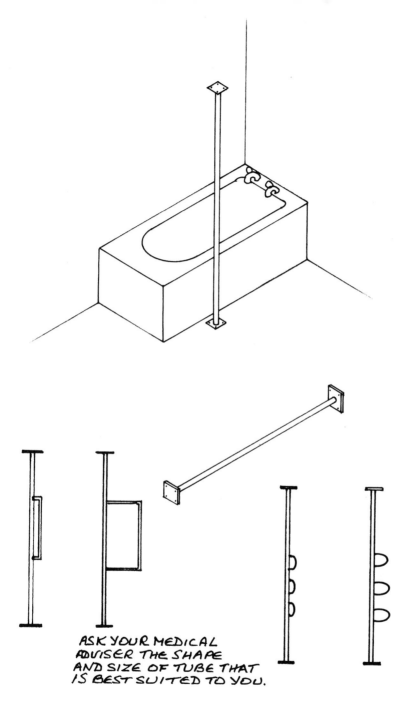

ASK YOUR MEDICAL
ADVISER THE SHAPE
AND SIZE OF TUBE THAT
IS BEST SUITED TO YOU.

129

BATH HANGER

This is a little aid that a young member of the family can make as a school project. In fact two can be made, one for beside the bath, as illustrated, and the other for hanging clothes and towel away from the bath and fixed at the right height.

Shopping List
A. Board: wood or plywood about 12 mm × 75 mm × 300 mm
    ($\frac{1}{2}'' \times 3'' \times 12''$)
B. Shelf: wood or plywood about 12 mm × 75 mm × 150 mm
    ($\frac{1}{2}'' \times 3'' \times 6''$)
C. Hooks: large chrome plated or plastic coated hooks

Instructions
1. Drill holes for wall fixing screws through board A.
2. Fix shelf B to board A if required.
3. Mark out and fix hooks C.
4. Fix hanger to the wall.

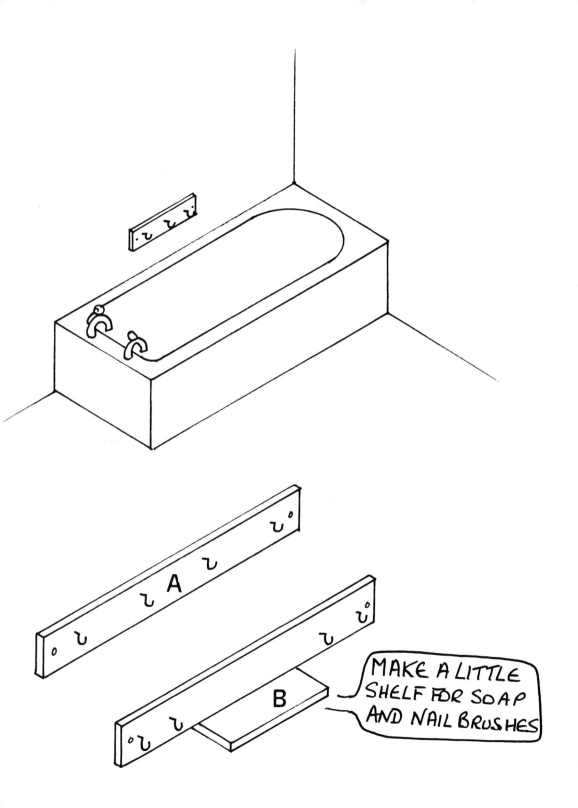

LARGE BATHROOM PLATFORM

A large platform which gives plenty of room on which to manoeuvre, and is also large enough to take a chair safely, can make it much easier to get in and out of the bath. The size will depend to a great extent on the floor space that can be used, but the width should not be less then 600 mm (24"); if it has to have a chair on it, this should be fixed to the floor with small metal brackets to prevent any risk of it slipping off. Even with a wide platform, it is a good idea to fix the chair if it has to be used as a support. The finished surface must be non-slip, whether it is wet or dry.

Shopping List (guide sizes)
A.   Top: external grade plywood or block board thick enough not to bend under your weight. Plywood 9 mm with extra support underneath. Block board 25 mm × 600 mm × 2 metres (1" × 24" × 6′ 6")
B.   Sides Long, 2 wanted: softwood 15 mm × 150 mm × 2 metres ($\frac{5}{8}$" × 6" × 6′ 6")
C.   Sides Short, 2 wanted: softwood 15 mm × 150 mm × 570 mm ($\frac{5}{8}$" × 6" × 22$\frac{3}{4}$")
D.   Corner Battens, 4 wanted: softwood 30 mm × 30 mm × 150 mm (1$\frac{1}{4}$" × 1$\frac{1}{4}$" × 6")
E.   Small Metal Brackets, 4 wanted

Construction: Glue and Nail, using waterproof glue

Instructions
1.   Assemble sides B and C using corner battens D.
2.   Fix top A to assembled base.
3.   Thoroughly paint. A non-slip surface must be used, even if it is only possible to put down rough coconut matting.
4.   Fix to floor with small metal brackets.

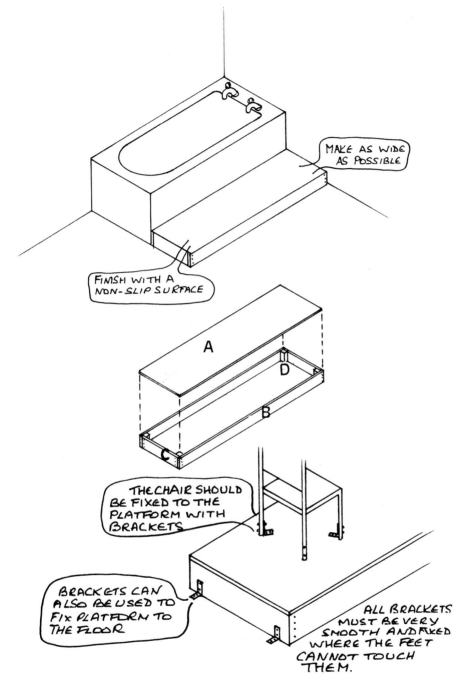

MAKE AS WIDE AS POSSIBLE

FINISH WITH A NON-SLIP SURFACE

A

D

B

C

THE CHAIR SHOULD BE FIXED TO THE PLATFORM WITH BRACKETS

BRACKETS CAN ALSO BE USED TO FIX PLATFORM TO THE FLOOR

ALL BRACKETS MUST BE VERY SMOOTH AND FIXED WHERE THE FEET CANNOT TOUCH THEM.

HANDRAILS

It is not always possible to buy a ready-made handrail which is exactly what is required, but this need not be a problem as they are not difficult to make. Welding can be done locally as most garages have the equipment; they will also be able to drill and countersink the holes. It is not essential to have the use of a pipe bending machine as in most cases a butt joint is just as good for achieving the required shape. Look at the illustrations for various ways of making handrails, but remember: no matter how good the rail is, it will be useless unless the wall and floor are strong enough to take the strain, so a careful examination by a professional is called for. As with the vertical handrail, other small metal tubes can be welded on to make it easier to hold. Make sure all welded joints are filed round and smooth before finishing.

134

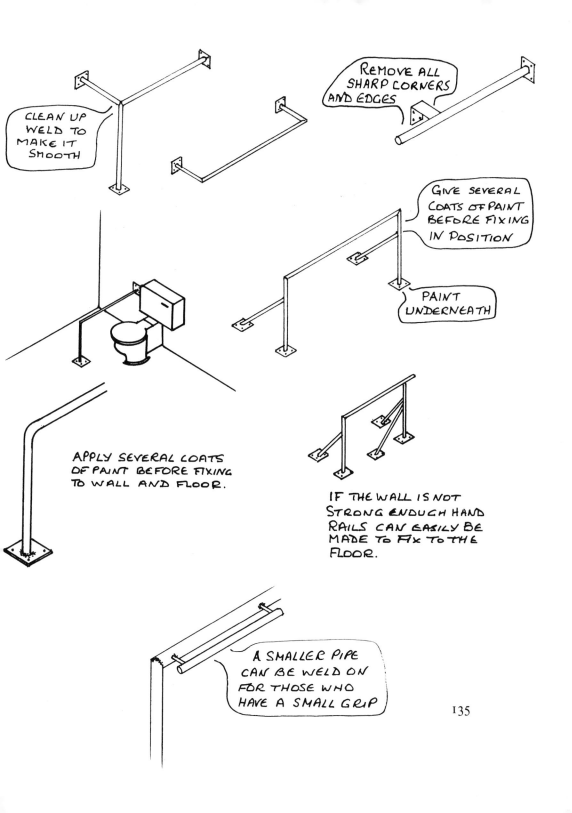

135

LAVATORY WALL PULL

A wall pull gives that little help sometimes needed when lowering oneself onto the lavatory and getting up from it. To derive maximum benefit from this aid, some time will have to be spent finding the best position for it. The wall must then be checked to make sure it is strong enough to take the strain when the pull is used. Similar pulls can be fitted elsewhere in the home where there is a convenient wall.

Shopping List
A. Handle: wooden dowel about 25 mm (1″) diameter × 150 mm (6″)
B. Eye Screw: heavy duty with a hole diameter of 25 mm (1″). Tell the supplier what it is to be used for
C. Rope: about 5 mm ($\frac{3}{16}$″) diameter

Instructions
1. Drill hole and plug it for eye screw B.
2. Drill 2 holes in handle A for rope C.
3. Glasspaper handle A to remove all sharp edges.
4. Thread rope C through eye screw B and handle A and knot as illustrated.
5. Screw eye screw into wall and check that the pull is strong enough.

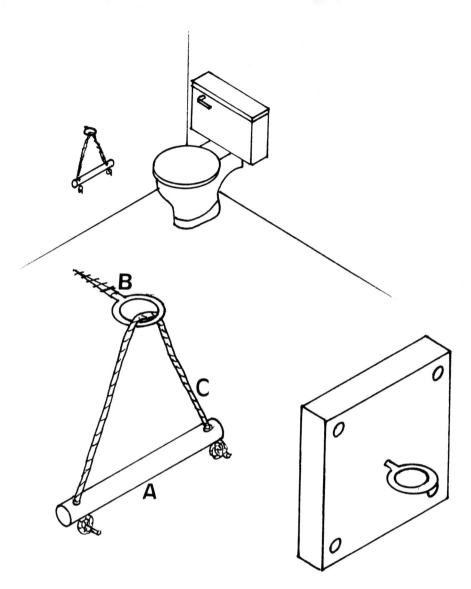

IF THE WALL IS NOT STRONG
ENOUGH FOR A RING SCREW
AND WALL PLUG, SCREW
RING SCREW INTO A THICK
PIECE OF WOOD. THIS WILL
SPREAD THE LOAD OVER A
LARGE AREA.

COMMODE

Try and find a chair which is not only the best height but also wide enough. The illustrations show some of the ways it can be converted so that it does not look conspicuous. If other people are likely to be in the room when it is being used, why not make a small screen to give a little privacy?

Shopping List
A. Seat: 9 mm plywood × size to fit chair
B. Shelf: 6 or 9 mm plywood × size to fit between chair legs
C. Shelf Brackets, 4 wanted: angle iron or angle aluminium
    3 mm × 25 mm × 25 mm × 25 mm ($\frac{1}{8}'' \times 1'' \times 1'' \times 1''$)
D. Self Tapping Screws, 16 wanted

Instructions
1. Remove existing seat from chair.
2. Make a paper pattern of the shape of the hole.
3. Mark out the hole shape on seat A.
4. Cut out hole shape in seat A.
5. Drill screw holes in seat A.
6. Glasspaper and paint seat A and shelf B with polyurethane paint.
7. Drill holes in chair legs for brackets C and fix them.
8. Fix seat A to chair.
9. Fix shelf B to chair legs.

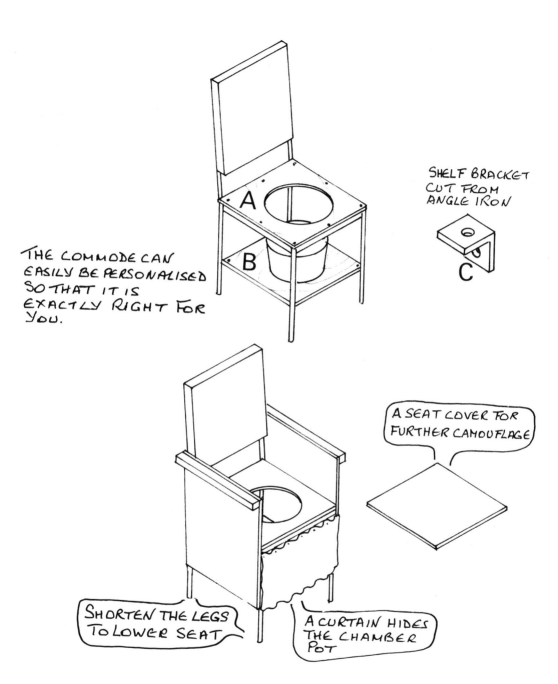

THE COMMODE CAN
EASILY BE PERSONALISED
SO THAT IT IS
EXACTLY RIGHT FOR
YOU.

A

B

SHELF BRACKET
CUT FROM
ANGLE IRON

C

A SEAT COVER FOR
FURTHER CAMOUFLAGE

SHORTEN THE LEGS
TO LOWER SEAT

A CURTAIN HIDES
THE CHAMBER
POT

139

MOBILE LAVATORY SEAT

The mobile lavatory seat allows a person to transfer to the seat from a bed or a chair and be pushed to the lavatory which can then be used without others being present. As a standard chair is used, it will easily go through the door and can be manoeuvred over the pan, making structural alterations unnecessary. The choice of the metal tube chair is important as it must have no cross pieces which would hit the pan; when the castors are fitted, the chair seat must have reasonable clearance over the top of the pan (see illustration on p. 142). A plastic seat can be bought and fitted instead of making a wooden one.

Shopping List
A. Seat: plywood 9 mm × size of the chair frame
B. Foot Rest: plywood 9 mm × 250 mm (10″) × inside leg measurement less 6 mm ($\frac{1}{4}$″)
C. Angle Irons, 2 wanted: 3 mm × 30 mm × 30 mm ($\frac{1}{8}$″ × 1$\frac{1}{4}$″ × 1$\frac{1}{4}$″) × distance between front and back legs plus 250 mm (10″)
D. Self Tapping Screws, 11 wanted: non rusting type
E. Nuts and Bolts, 4 wanted: about 3 mm diameter × 20mm ($\frac{1}{4}$″ × $\frac{3}{4}$″)
F. Castors, 4 wanted

Instructions for Making and Fixing Wooden Seat
1. Remove existing seat from chair.
2. Paint the metal chair frame with polyurethane paint.
3. Make a paper pattern of the hole and mark out on the seat A.
4. Cut the hole and round edge in seat A.
5. Drill holes for screws in seat A.
6. Glasspaper and paint with polyurethane.
7. Fix seat A to chair frame.
8. Fix castors to chair legs.

Instructions for Foot Rest (illustrated overleaf)

1. Drill chair legs for foot rest angle irons C.
2. Drill foot rest angle irons C so that holes line up with chair leg holes.
3. Paint foot rest angle irons C.
4. Fix foot rest angle irons C to chair legs.
5. Fix foot rest B to foot rest angle irons C.
6. Fix front castors to front of foot rest as illustrated.

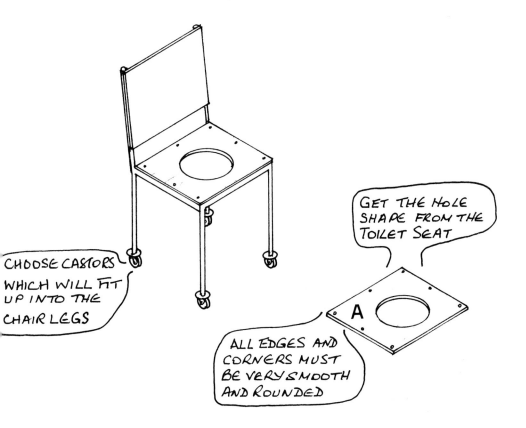

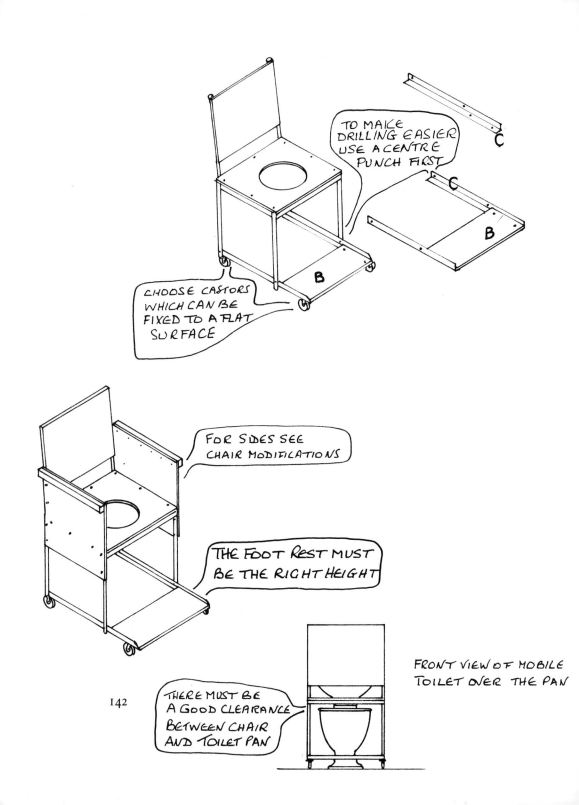

142

HALL, STAIRS AND LANDING

The hall can be a cold and draughty place so make sure all the doors and windows fit well or have draught excluders. The front door should be looked at very carefully as this is where most of the cold air is coming from. Besides draught excluders, a heavy curtain can help a lot, and it will also cover the letter box. These are jobs members of the family can do. They can also check for uneven and loose floorboards, carry out the wardrobe modifications to the hall clothes cupboard and fit a safety security chain at the right height. For peace of mind, start fitting security locks to all downstairs windows and doors, and have those locks which are already there refitted so that they are easier to use. Have all the light switches placed close to the front door so that lights can be put on as the front door is opened.

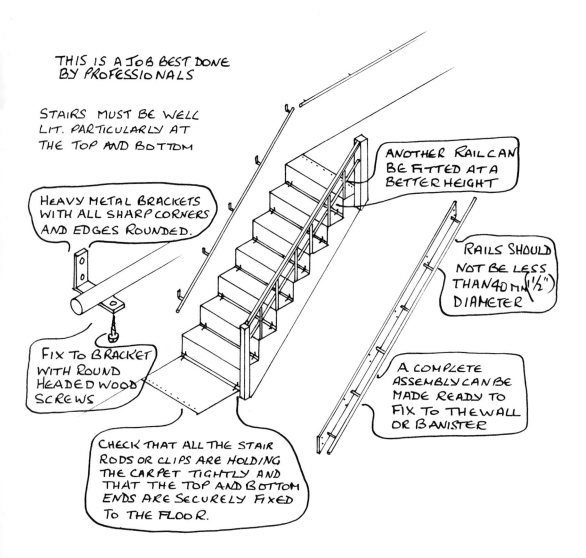

THIS IS A JOB BEST DONE
BY PROFESSIONALS

STAIRS MUST BE WELL
LIT. PARTICULARLY AT
THE TOP AND BOTTOM

ANOTHER RAIL CAN
BE FITTED AT A
BETTER HEIGHT

HEAVY METAL BRACKETS
WITH ALL SHARP CORNERS
AND EDGES ROUNDED.

RAILS SHOULD
NOT BE LESS
THAN 40mm (1½")
DIAMETER

FIX TO BRACKET
WITH ROUND
HEADED WOOD
SCREWS

A COMPLETE
ASSEMBLY CAN BE
MADE READY TO
FIX TO THE WALL
OR BANISTER

CHECK THAT ALL THE STAIR
RODS OR CLIPS ARE HOLDING
THE CARPET TIGHTLY AND
THAT THE TOP AND BOTTOM
ENDS ARE SECURELY FIXED
TO THE FLOOR.

144

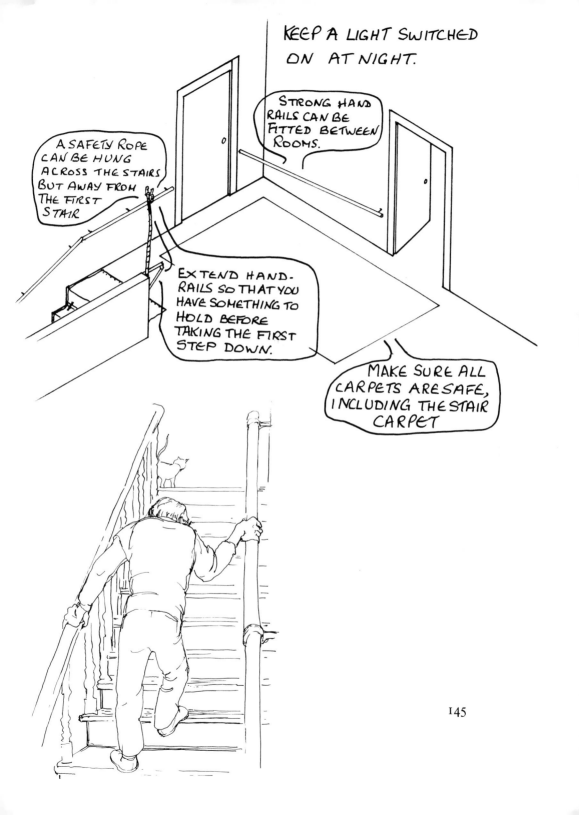

145

DOOR STOPS

There is always a chance of a sudden gust of wind making the door slam when you are on the wrong side of it. This door stop hangs by the front or back door and can be put in position without any effort, so that you are never locked out. Don't buy any special stuffing as rolled up old clothes are quite good enough, and if it's not heavy enough add a few stones.

Doors inside the home may also be fitted with stops and some of the ways these can be made are illustrated. To save having to bend down, a cord and hooks screwed into the wall or door will always keep them to hand.

Shopping List
A.   Any piece of strong cloth at least 230 mm × 300 mm (9″ × 12″)
B.   String, length according to requirements

Instructions
1.   Sew cloth to make a tube 115 mm diameter × 300 mm ($4\frac{1}{2}$″ × 12″).
2.   Stuff and sew up ends.
3.   Sew on loops for string.
4.   Attach string as illustrated.
5.   Fix a hook beside the door and hang on door stop as illustrated.

STUFF WITH ANY SOFT MATERIAL

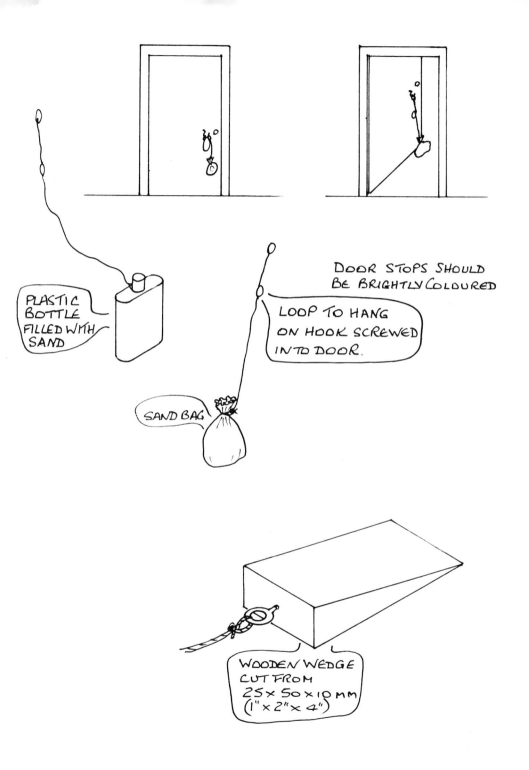

GETTING FROM ROOM TO ROOM

When you have difficulty moving about, it is important to be well organised, so that you do not have to make a lot of unnecessary journeys to and fro, to fetch articles you need. Bags can be fitted to any walking aid you may use, to hold small, light objects, and well-stocked trolleys will provide both support and a handy way of transporting everything required for a particular job. The pocketed aprons and belts described in the Kitchen and Garden sections will also be helpful.

CLEANING HELP

The Cleaning Help is really a small wheeled walker with a shelf and tray. It will carry all the cleaning materials from room to room to save a lot of 'toing and froing' for forgotten things. If going up stairs is difficult, have a second one up there and keep it in a cupboard out of sight when not in use. A few hooks round the tray side can be used to hang cleaning rags, dusters and other things which have a string or tape loop. The shelf must not be too wide or you will bark your shins when walking, but there must be a shelf as it gives rigidity to the legs. If the cleaning help has to be made higher or lower don't forget to add in the height of the castors, and if it has to be made wider or narrower, remember that all the other pieces will have a different length.

Shopping List

A. Back legs, 2 wanted: softwood 40 mm × 40 mm × 700 mm
    ($1\frac{1}{2}'' \times 1\frac{1}{2}'' \times 27''$)
B. Front Legs, 2 wanted: softwood 40 mm × 40 mm × 700 mm
    ($1\frac{1}{2}'' \times 1\frac{1}{2}'' \times 27''$)
C. Sides, 4 wanted: softwood 12 mm × 40 mm × 300 mm
    ($\frac{1}{2}'' \times 1\frac{1}{2}'' \times 12''$)
D. Shelf: plywood 4 mm × 150 mm × 300 mm ($6'' \times 12''$)
E. Shelf and Tray Fronts, 2 wanted: softwood
    12 mm × 40 mm × 300 mm ($\frac{1}{2}'' \times 1\frac{1}{2}'' \times 12''$)
F. Tray: plywood 4 mm × 300 mm × 300 mm ($12'' \times 12''$)
G. Cup Hooks, 6–8 wanted
H. Castors, 4 wanted. The wheels should be about 2'' diameter

Construction: Glue and Nail

Instructions

1. Cut a 45° angle to the top of legs A.
2. Fix sides C to legs A and B, the lower ones 300 mm (12″) from the top.
3. Fix fronts E to legs B, the top one to the outside and the lower one to the inside.
4. Cut the corners of tray F to fit round the legs A and B.
5. Turn upside down and fit tray F and shelf D.
6. Fit castors.
7. Remove all sharp corners and edges and glasspaper.
8. Paint or varnish.

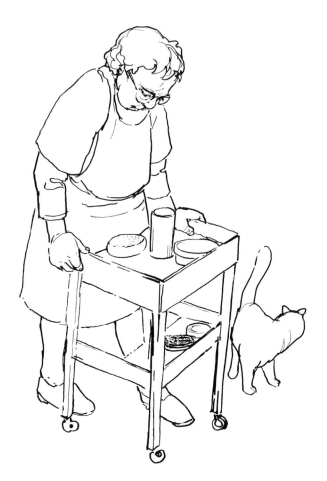

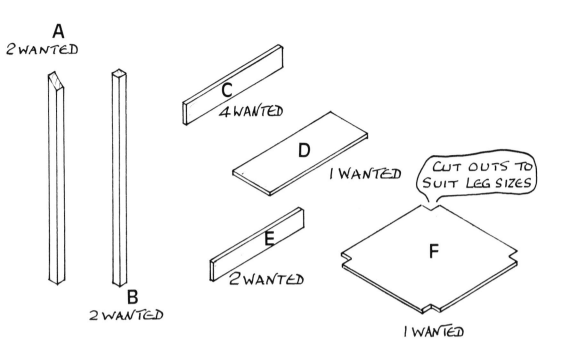

A
2 WANTED

B
2 WANTED

C
4 WANTED

D
1 WANTED

E
2 WANTED

CUT OUTS TO SUIT LEG SIZES

F
1 WANTED

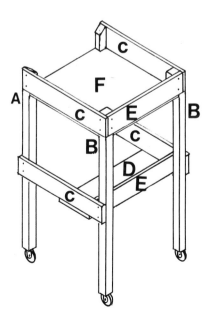

IF THE UNSUPPORTED TRAY EDGE IS NOT STRONG ENOUGH ADD A BATTEN 25 × 25 (1"×1") MM   MM

151

BAG FOR FRAME WALKER

A suitable bag for a walker can easily be found in the shops and adapted to fit to the top rail. A string lacing is nearly always good enough, but it must also be fixed at the bottom to stop the bag swinging.

STICK BAG

Like the crutch bag overleaf, it must not be made too big and should only be used for small light articles. The metal clip may have to be made by the local garage, but look into the hardwear shop first.

Shopping List
A. Bag Support: plywood 6 mm × 25 mm × 150 mm (1″ × 6″)
B. Metal Clip. The size will depend on the diameter of the stick
C. Nut and Bolt, 2 wanted: round headed, about 12 mm ($\frac{1}{2}$″) long. The diameter to suit the hole in the metal clip B
D. Bag Cloth: 150 mm wide × 300 mm long (6″ × 12″)
E. String for lacing

Instructions
1. Drill holes for metal clip nuts C.
2. Drill holes for string E.
3. Make bag D.
4. Lace bag D to bag support A.
5. Fix bag to stick.

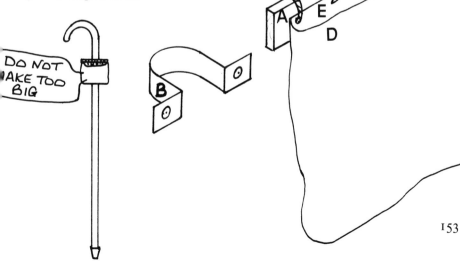

DO NOT MAKE TOO BIG

153

CRUTCH BAG

Most crutches can be fitted with this little bag which can hold a few personal things. If money or valuables are to be carried, it is advisable to fit a zip or at least a button to help to protect them. Don't make the bag too big or put too much in it, as the extra weight might make it difficult to walk and you may also upset your medical adviser.

The bag can either be laced or nailed to the front clamping piece.

Shopping List
A. Clamping Strips, 2 wanted: softwood 12 mm × 40 mm × the outside width of the crutch plus 50 mm ($\frac{1}{2}''$ × $1\frac{1}{2}''$ × the outside width of the crutch plus 2″)
B. Nut and Bolt, 2 of each wanted. The length will be the thickness of the crutch plus 24 mm plus 12 mm (plus 1″ plus $\frac{1}{2}''$). Try and buy roofing nuts and bolts as these have a round head which will not catch on your clothing.
C. Cloth to make a small bag about 180 mm wide × 400 mm long (7″ × 16″).
D. Round Headed Upholstery Nails, about 10.

Instructions
1. Drill the holes for the nuts and bolts B through clamping strips A.
2. Sew up bag C.
3. Nail or lace to front clamping strip.
4. Clamp to crutch, making sure that the smooth round headed bolt head is on the body.

TIE THE BOTTOM OF THE BAG TO THE CRUTCH TO STOP IT SWINGING ABOUT

A

B

A

C

155

OUTSIDE THE HOUSE AND IN THE GARDEN

If you find yourself becoming less mobile, there are many simple but effective adaptations you can make which will allow you to go out and about as much as you like. A ramp will overcome difficulties in negotiating steps, a little shelf for milk will mean you will not have to worry about bending down to pick it up, and a letter box will catch all the mail before it lands on the floor.

In the garden, there is no limit to the changes that can be made to enable you to enjoy tending your plants. Bring the flowerbeds up to your level, fix handrails along paths, make use of hanging baskets and tables. Gardening is one activity that is infinitely adaptable and should never be beyond your reach, no matter how disabled you may be.

RAMPS

Ramps should always be made and fixed in position by a local contractor unless there is a member of the family who has the necessary skills. This is one of those jobs which looks easy but is not, and any fixing which has to be done to the building can prove expensive should the wall or step be damaged. If the ramp is not securely fixed at both ends, gaps and unevenness will appear sooner or later.

The angle or slope of the ramp should be as shallow as space will permit, whether it is to be used by a wheelchair or walking up and down. The treatment of the surface is very important; it does not matter what weather conditions are likely to prevail, it must safe or easily made safe to walk on. Sand scattered onto wet paint can give a non-slip surface, but it soon wears smooth. Whatever treatment is given it must be regularly inspected. A builder can make a permanent job using cement and make the surface non-slip before it sets.

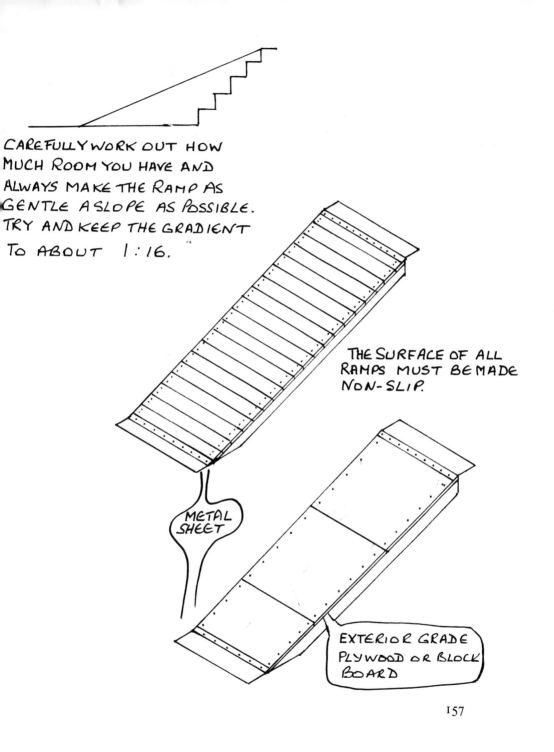

CAREFULLY WORK OUT HOW
MUCH ROOM YOU HAVE AND
ALWAYS MAKE THE RAMP AS
GENTLE A SLOPE AS POSSIBLE.
TRY AND KEEP THE GRADIENT
TO ABOUT 1:16.

THE SURFACE OF ALL
RAMPS MUST BE MADE
NON-SLIP.

METAL
SHEET

EXTERIOR GRADE
PLYWOOD OR BLOCK
BOARD

157

MILK SHELF

A shelf by the front or back door can save a lot of bending down, because all deliveries can be left on it. A stiff length of thick wire or strip of metal can be bent round as illustrated to stop light packages blowing off.

Shopping List
A. Shelf: softwood 20 mm × 150 mm × 300 mm ($\frac{3}{4}''$ × 6″ × 12″)
B. Brackets, 2 wanted: strong, well painted shelf brackets to take a 150 mm (12″) wide shelf
C. Rail: stiff, thick wire or metal strip 2 mm × 12 mm × 685 mm ($\frac{3}{32}''$ × $\frac{1}{2}''$ × 27″)
D. Clothes Peg to hold notes

Instructions
1. Fix brackets B to shelf A.
2. Mark wall for screws.
3. Paint shelf A.
4. Drill and plug wall for screws.
5. Fix shelf to wall and check that it is strong enough.
6. Bend the wire to shape or drill and bend the metal strip and shape as illustrated to make the rail.
7. Paint the rail.
8. Fix the clothes peg as illustrated.

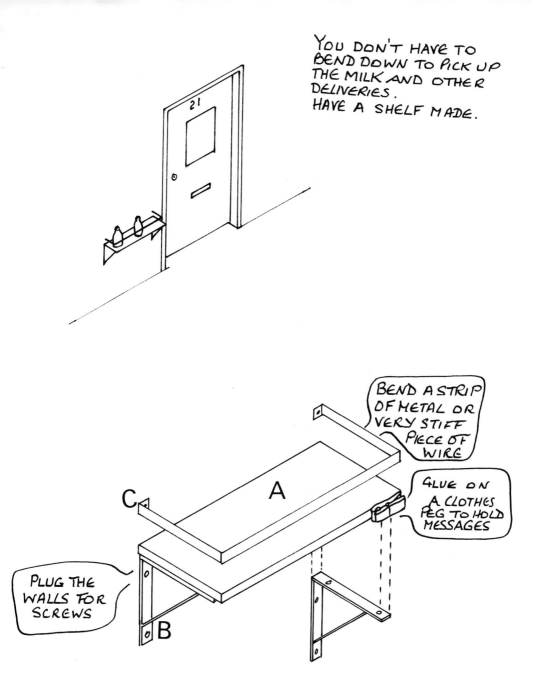

LETTER BOX

Another aid to save bending down is a box to catch letters and newspapers. If there is no room for a box because the door opens against a wall, an illustration shows how to make a box from soft foam plastic which will flatten when it touches the wall.

Shopping List (all pieces cut from one plank)
A. Sides, 2 wanted: softwood 12 mm × 150 mm × 300 mm ($\frac{1}{2}'' \times 6'' \times 12''$)
B. Front: softwood 12 mm × 300 mm × 300 mm ($\frac{1}{2}'' \times 12'' \times 12''$)
C. Base: softwood 12 mm × 150 mm × 300 mm ($\frac{1}{2}'' \times 6'' \times 12''$)
D. Brackets, 4 wanted: see illustration

Shopping List for Foam Plastic
A. Fairly stiff plastic foam sheet about 25 mm (1″) thick, all other sizes as above

Construction: Glue and Nail

Instructions
1. To make front B, glue 2 pieces of wood together.
2. Fix sides A to front B.
3. Fix base C to assembled sides A and front B.
4. Fix brackets to sides A.
5. Glasspaper and paint to match door.
6. Fix finished box to door.

LETTERS DON'T HAVE TO DROP ON THE MAT. HAVE A BOX FITTED.

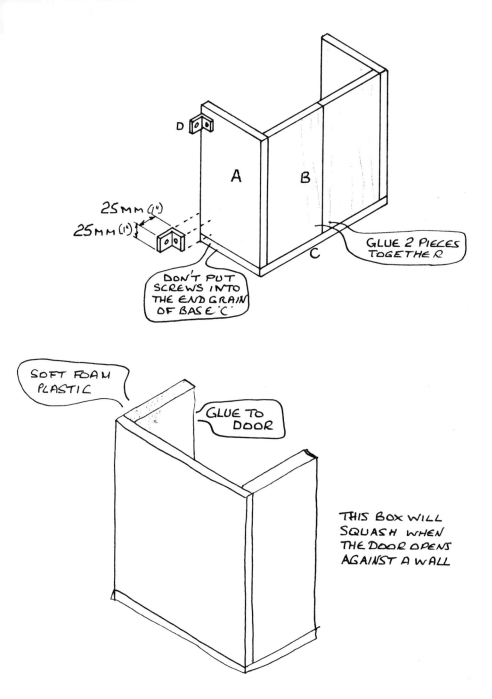

D

25MM (1")
25MM (1")

A

B

C

DON'T PUT
SCREWS INTO
THE END GRAIN
OF BASE 'C'

GLUE 2 PIECES
TOGETHER

SOFT FOAM
PLASTIC

GLUE TO
DOOR

THIS BOX WILL
SQUASH WHEN
THE DOOR OPENS
AGAINST A WALL

GARDEN KNEELER

As you grow older the ground seems to be further away. A kneeler that enables you to get down to the low gardening jobs, as well as helping you up to a standing position again, may make it possible for you to continue gardening for a long time to come. It is important to get the measurement for the kneeler right and it may be necessary to change the height of the side.

Shopping List

A.   Sides, 2 wanted: softwood 15 mm × 200 mm × 400 mm ($\frac{5}{8}'' \times 8'' \times 16''$)

B.   Kneeling Board: softwood 15 mm × 200 mm × 355 mm ($\frac{5}{8}'' \times 8'' \times 14''$)

C.   Kneeling Board Battens, 2 wanted: softwood 25 mm × 25 mm × 200 mm ($1'' \times 1'' \times 8''$)

D.   Base: softwood 15 mm × 200 mm × 355 mm ($\frac{5}{8}'' \times 8'' \times 14''$)

E.   Base Battens, 2 wanted: softwood 25 mm × 25 mm × 200 mm ($1'' \times 1'' \times 8''$)

F.   Support: softwood 15 mm × to suit kneeling height × 355 mm ($\frac{5}{8}'' \times$ to suit kneeling height $\times 14''$)

G.   Support Battens, 2 wanted: 25 mm × 25 mm × 255 mm ($1'' \times 1'' \times 10''$)

Construction: Waterproof Glue and Screw

Instructions

1. Fix kneeling board battens C to sides A at kneeling height.
2. Fix battens E to base D.
3. Fix support battens G to support F.
4. Fix sides A to assembled base D.
5. Fix support F to centre of base D and knee board B.

162

6. Fix kneeling board B to sides A and support F.
7. Glasspaper and paint.
8. Pad top edges of sides A.
9. Pad kneeling board.

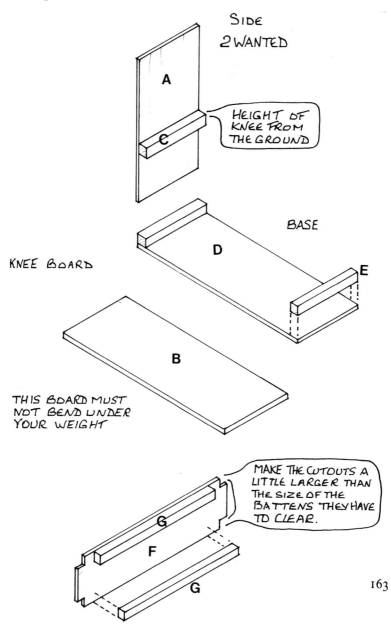

SIDE
2 WANTED

A

C

HEIGHT OF KNEE FROM THE GROUND

BASE

D

E

KNEE BOARD

B

THIS BOARD MUST NOT BEND UNDER YOUR WEIGHT

MAKE THE CUTOUTS A LITTLE LARGER THAN THE SIZE OF THE BATTENS THEY HAVE TO CLEAR.

G

F

G

163

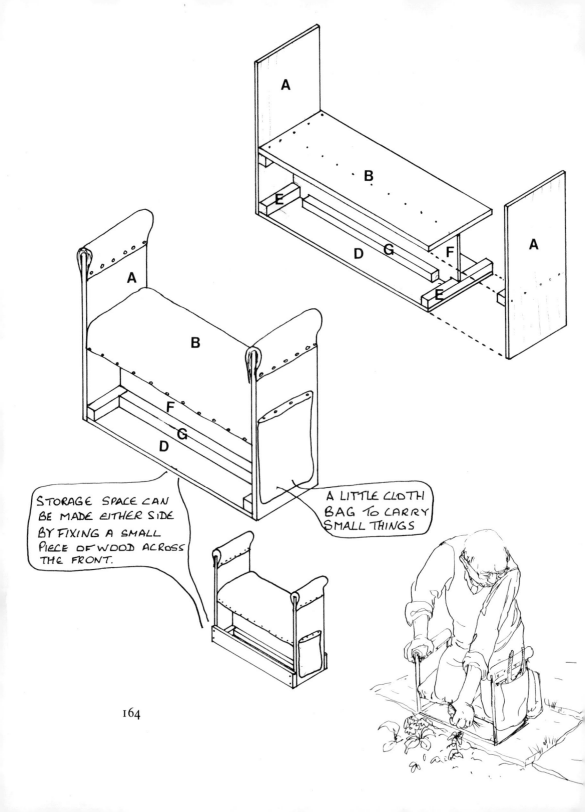

A

B

E

D G

F

A

A

B

F

G

D

STORAGE SPACE CAN
BE MADE EITHER SIDE
BY FIXING A SMALL
PIECE OF WOOD ACROSS
THE FRONT.

A LITTLE CLOTH
BAG TO CARRY
SMALL THINGS

164

BOOT AND SHOE CLEANER

It's not a good idea to go into the house with dirty boots and leave the floor covered with muddy foot marks. Keep these cleaners hanging somewhere handy for use on those days when the soil is sticky.

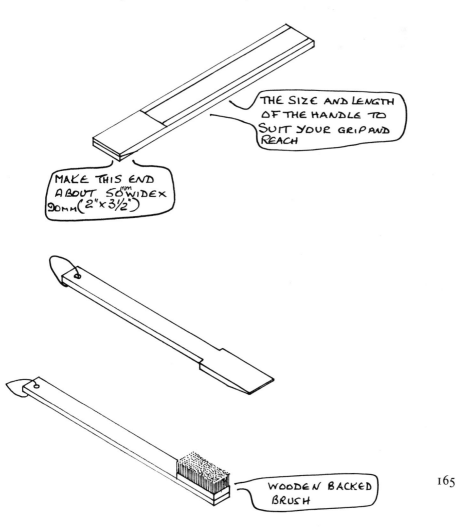

THE SIZE AND LENGTH OF THE HANDLE TO SUIT YOUR GRIP AND REACH

MAKE THIS END ABOUT 50mm WIDE x 90mm (2" x 3½")

WOODEN BACKED BRUSH

GARDENING SEAT AND TOOL BOX

There are lots of gardening jobs which can be done while sitting down on a low, comfortable seat. This seat also holds a few tools, which can save you going backwards and forwards to the shed to fetch the ones that have been forgotten. A rope is tied to one end so that it can be pulled along.

Shopping List
A. Top: softwood 15 mm × 200 mm × 300 mm ($\frac{5}{8}'' \times 8'' \times 12''$)
B. Sides, 2 wanted: softwood 15 mm × 200 mm × 200 mm ($\frac{5}{8}'' \times 8'' \times 8''$)
C. Back: softwood 15 mm × 200 mm × 330 mm ($\frac{5}{8}'' \times 8'' \times 13\frac{1}{4}''$)
D. Base: softwood 15 mm × 200 mm × 270 mm ($\frac{5}{8}'' \times 8'' \times 10\frac{3}{4}''$)
E. Front: softwood 15 mm × 70 mm × 330 mm ($\frac{5}{8}'' \times 2\frac{3}{4}'' \times 13\frac{1}{4}''$)

Construction: Glue and Screw

Instructions
1. Drill 2 holes for rope in side B.
2. Fix sides B to base D.
3. Fix back C to assembled base D.
4. Fix front E to assembled base D.
5. Fix top A to sides B and back C.
6. Glasspaper and paint.
7. Pad top A. The padding should be covered with strong cloth.

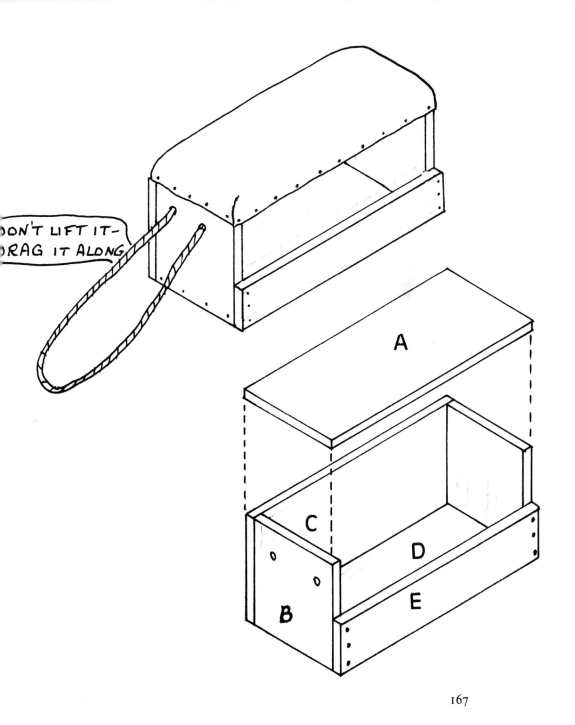

KNEELING PAD

Kneeling can be tough on the knees, but a thick pad can be a great help. The choice of padding is important because if the knees go too far into it you will soon start to feel all the stones again. As the grass and soil are usually damp, it's a good idea to make one side of waterproof material, so that the padding will keep dry.

Shopping List
A. Strong cloth such as canvas: about 300 mm × 460 mm (12″ × 18″)
B. Waterproof cloth: about 230 mm × 300 mm (9″ × 12″)
C. Padding

Instructions
1. Fold cloth A in half to make a bag 230 mm × 300 mm (9″ × 12″).
2. Sew together along one short side and the long side to make an open ended bag.
3. Sew waterproof cloth on to one side.
4. Evenly fill the bag, making sure that it is firm and sew up remaining sides.
5. Sew on handle.

If a polythene bag is used as an inner waterproof bag it must have some holes on the top side to let the air out.

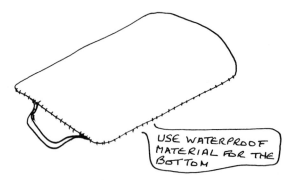

USE WATERPROOF MATERIAL FOR THE BOTTOM

HANDRAILS

Always buy wood which you find good to hold. This need not necessarily be round or 'D' shaped, but it must be smooth and completely free of splits, twists and splinters. The posts must be pointed at one end and long enough to be driven well into the ground. The complete structure must be strong enough to take your weight should you stumble.

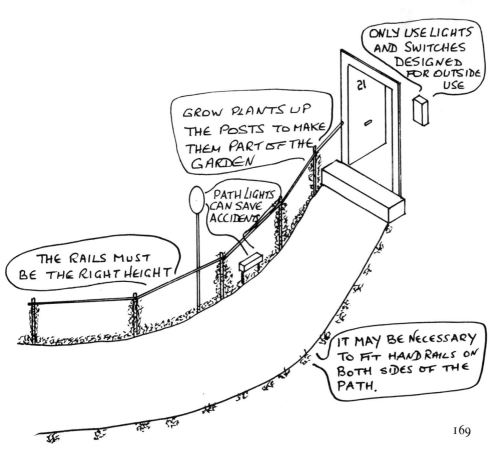

GARDEN ADAPTATIONS

If you have a garden or an allotment, there is nothing to stop you making or having made a few aids and planning a few changes to the garden layout which will enable you to go on getting pleasure from growing things. Much of the heavy work may have to be left to others, but a few ideas are given on the following pages which may help you to go on enjoying this wonderful pastime for a long time.

PLASTIC BAGS OF SOIL

PLANTS SHO
BE SUPPORT
WITH STRI

MAKE SURE THAT
THE WOODWORK IS
STRONG ENOUGH
TO TAKE YOUR
WEIGHT WHEN
YOU LEAN ON IT.

HANG POTS FROM
HOOKS OR BENT
STRONG NAILS.

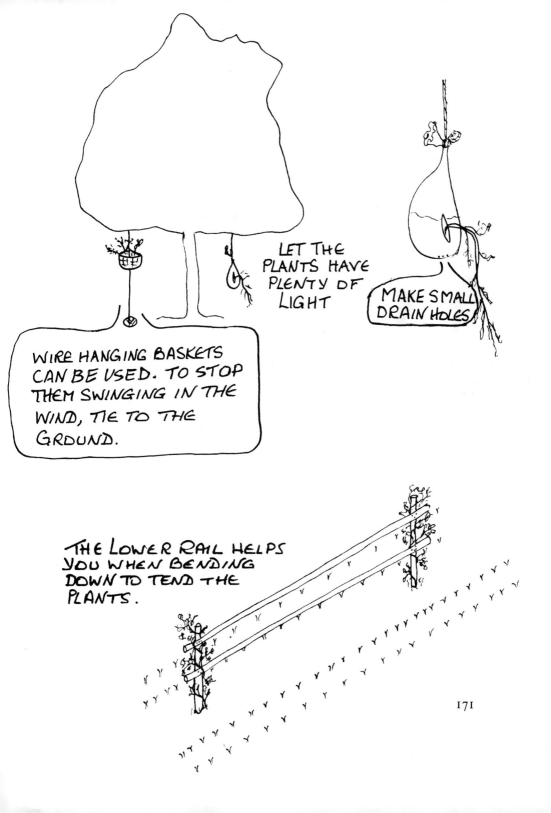

LET THE PLANTS HAVE PLENTY OF LIGHT

MAKE SMALL DRAIN HOLES

WIRE HANGING BASKETS CAN BE USED. TO STOP THEM SWINGING IN THE WIND, TIE TO THE GROUND.

THE LOWER RAIL HELPS YOU WHEN BENDING DOWN TO TEND THE PLANTS.

171

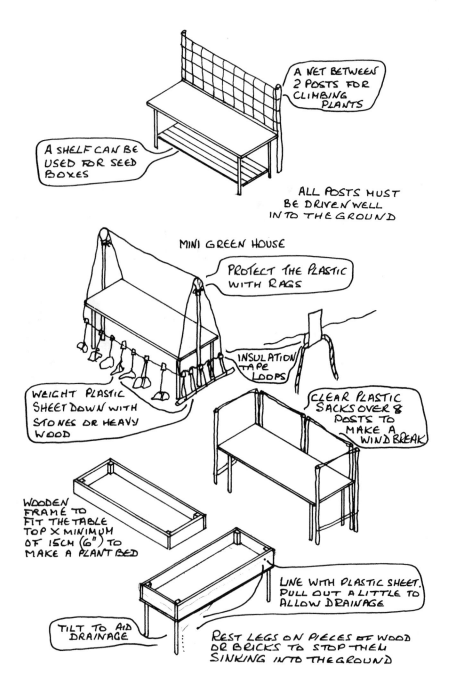

A NET BETWEEN 2 POSTS FOR CLIMBING PLANTS

A SHELF CAN BE USED FOR SEED BOXES

ALL POSTS MUST BE DRIVEN WELL INTO THE GROUND

MINI GREEN HOUSE

PROTECT THE PLASTIC WITH RAGS

INSULATION TAPE LOOPS

WEIGHT PLASTIC SHEET DOWN WITH STONES OR HEAVY WOOD

CLEAR PLASTIC SACKS OVER 8 POSTS TO MAKE A WINDBREAK

WOODEN FRAME TO FIT THE TABLE TOP X MINIMUM OF 15CM (6") TO MAKE A PLANT BED

LINE WITH PLASTIC SHEET. PULL OUT A LITTLE TO ALLOW DRAINAGE

TILT TO AID DRAINAGE

REST LEGS ON PIECES OF WOOD OR BRICKS TO STOP THEM SINKING INTO THE GROUND

172

A PLASTIC SHEET HELPS TO KEEP THE TABLE CLEAN.

IF THE TABLE IS TOO HIGH, MAKE THE LEGS SHORTER BY CUTTING OR SINKING THEM INTO THE GROUND.

PAD THE TOPS OF THE POSTS AND TIE A STRONG STRING BETWEEN THEM.

A NET OVER THE PLASTIC SHEET PROTECTS IT DURING WINDY WEATHER.

THE POSTS ARE HELD WITH SMALL METAL BRACKETS

173

FOUR WHEELED BOX TROLLEY

A little trolley to carry tools and things can save a lot of trips back to the toolshed and it can also be used to bring home the harvest. Details are given on how to make a box, but any reasonably strong one can be used. The wheels should be large, with a wide tread, but if the ground is very rough it may be better to fit skids as illustrated. It is not always necessary to make a trolley with front-wheel steering, but it does help if pulling is a problem.

Shopping List for Box Trolley
A.   Axle, 2 wanted: metal tube or rod to suit wheels and width of box
B.   Brackets, 4 wanted: pipe brackets or bend a piece of stiff metal
C.   Box Bottom, 2 pieces wanted: softwood
     20 mm × 150 mm × 450 mm ($\frac{3}{4}'' \times 6'' \times 18''$)
D.   Box Sides, 2 wanted: softwood 20 mm × 150 mm × 450 mm
     ($\frac{3}{4}'' \times 6'' \times 18''$)
E.   Box Ends, 2 wanted: softwood 20 mm × 150 mm × 262 mm
     ($\frac{3}{4}'' \times 6'' \times 10\frac{1}{2}''$)
F.   Skids when wheels are not used, 2 wanted: softwood
     20 mm × 150 mm × 450 mm ($\frac{3}{4}'' \times 6'' \times 18''$)
G.   Wheels, 4 needed: any with wide tread, minimum diameter
     100 mm ($4''$)

Instructions for Box Trolley
1.   Assemble box as illustrated on p. 176.
2.   Fix brackets B about 75 mm ($3''$) from each end as illustrated.
3.   Drill a small hole at each end of axles A to hold fixing wire.
4.   Slide axles A through brackets B.
5.   Fix on wheels and insert wire in axle holes to hold them in place.
6.   Drill holes for tow rope.

Shopping List for Steered Trolley

A. Axle, 2 wanted: metal tube or rod to suit wheels, width of box and board

B. Axle Brackets, 4 wanted: to suit axles

C. Box Bottom, 2 pieces wanted: softwood 20 mm × 150 mm × 450 mm ($\frac{3}{4}'' \times 6'' \times 18''$)

D. Box Sides, 2 wanted: softwood 20 mm × 150 mm × 450 mm ($\frac{3}{4}'' \times 6'' \times 18''$)

E. Box Ends, 2 wanted: softwood 20 mm × 150 mm × 262 mm ($\frac{3}{4}'' \times 6'' \times 10\frac{1}{2}''$)

F. Board: softwood about 20 mm × 250 mm × 800 mm ($\frac{3}{4}'' \times 10'' \times 32''$)

G. Axle Board: softwood 20 mm × 75 mm × width of box plus 50 mm ($\frac{3}{4}'' \times 3'' \times$ width of box plus 2'')

H. Bolt, 2 Washers and 2 Nuts: bolt length to suit total thickness of wood plus washers and nuts

I. Wheels, 4 wanted: as for box trolley

Instructions for Steered Trolley

1. Drill board F to be a good fit for bolt H.
2. Drill axle board G for bolt H and tow ropes.
3. Fix brackets B to axle board G.
4. Fix brackets B to back of box.
5. Fix board F so that it does not get in the way of axle—allow 90 mm ($3\frac{1}{2}''$).
6. Fix axles and wheels as for box trolley.
7. Bolt axle board G to board F so that it can move easily.
8. Tie on tow rope.

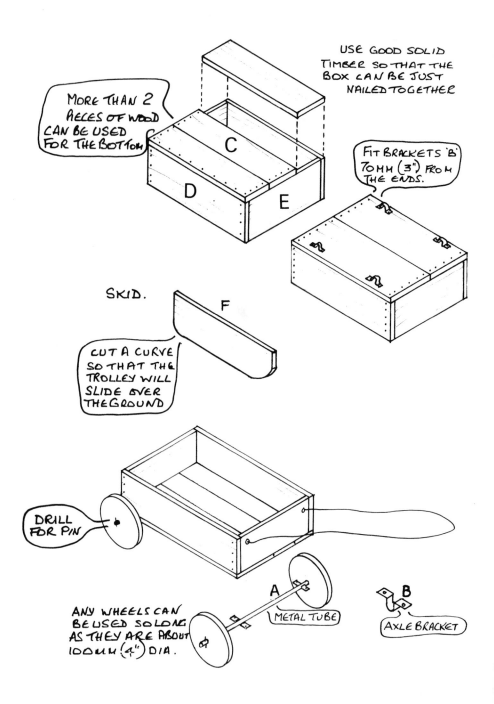

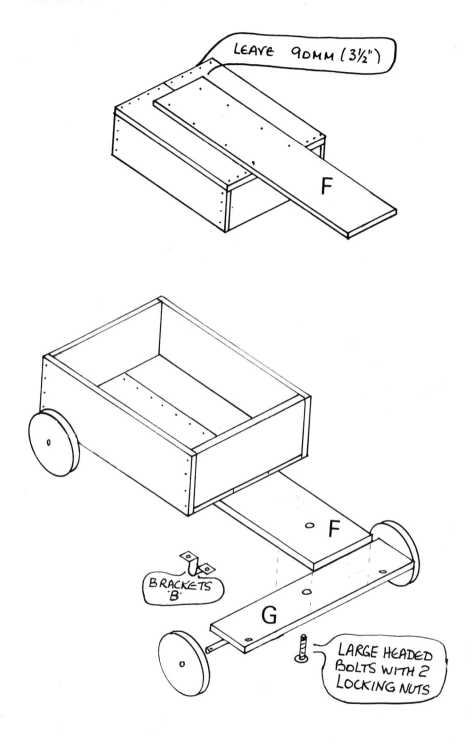

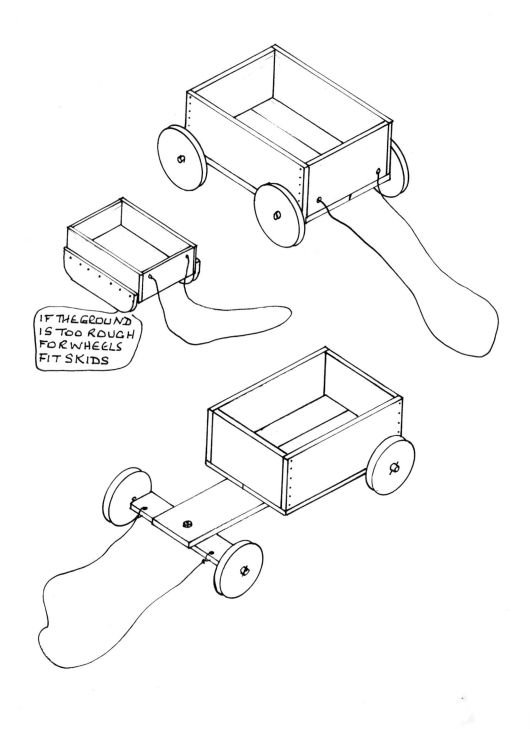

IF THE GROUND
IS TOO ROUGH
FOR WHEELS
FIT SKIDS

TWO WHEELED TROLLEY

A two wheeled trolley is sometimes easier to manoeuvre than a four wheeled one. As all the weight is to be borne on two wheels it is advisable to use large wide ones which will not sink into the soft soil so much. Wooden boxes can be obtained from some wine stores.

Shopping List
A.   Towing Arm: softwood 12 mm × 75 mm × about 900 mm ($\frac{1}{2}'' \times 3'' \times 35\frac{1}{2}''$)
B.   Handle: softwood 25 mm × 40 mm × 230 mm ($1'' \times 1\frac{1}{2}'' \times 9''$)
C.   Stop: softwood 25 mm × 75 mm × 75 mm ($1'' \times 3'' \times 3''$)
D.   Brackets, 2 wanted: to suit axle
See Four Wheeled Trolley for details of box

Instructions
1.   Fix handle B to towing arm A.
2.   Fix stop C to towing arm A.
3.   Fix assembled towing arm down centre line of box bottom. See illustration overleaf for other information.
4.   Fix wheel axle to box with brackets D (see illustrations).

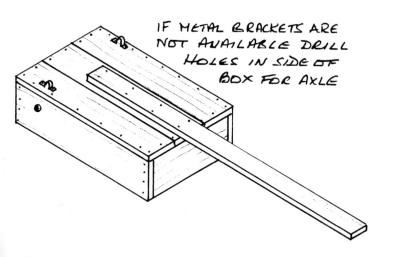

IF METAL BRACKETS ARE
NOT AVAILABLE DRILL
HOLES IN SIDE OF
BOX FOR AXLE

179

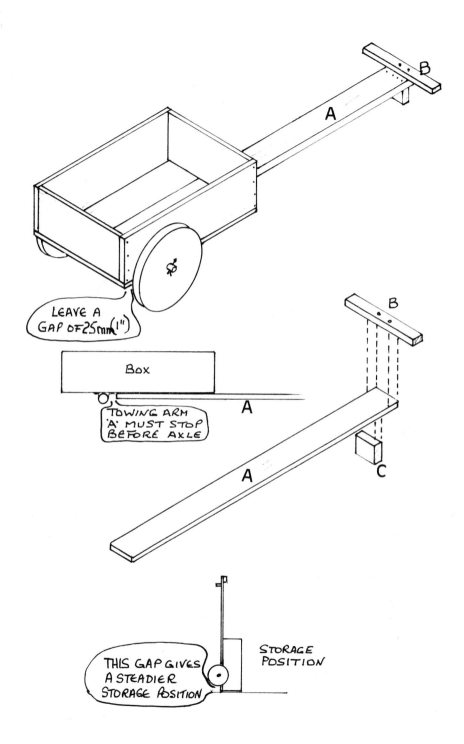

LEAVE A GAP OF 25mm (1")

Box

TOWING ARM 'A' MUST STOP BEFORE AXLE

A

A

B

C

THIS GAP GIVES A STEADIER STORAGE POSITION

STORAGE POSITION

CANVAS BELT WITH POCKETS

A simple belt with pockets which can be used in the garden as well as around the house when doing odd jobs. It is also a very useful belt to wear for some hobbies.

Shopping List
A.   A length of canvas or strong cloth about 200 mm × 500 mm (8″ × 20″)

Instructions
1. Hem both long sides of canvas.
2. Fold canvas in half lengthwise and sew pockets.
3. Sew on 2 loops of canvas as illustrated for tapes or string.

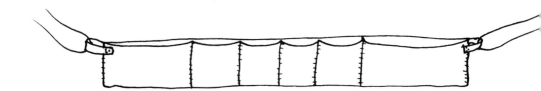

CLOTH BELT WITH POCKETS AND HOOKS

Sometimes a belt on which can hang secateurs, scissors or a knife, plus a few little pockets to put odds and ends in, is all that is needed when pottering about the garden.

Shopping List
A. Length of canvas or strong cloth about 500 mm long × 75 mm wide (20″ × 3″ wide)
B. Length of cloth for bags about 200 mm × 300 mm (8″ × 12″). This will make 4 bags of 75 mm × 100 mm (3″ × 4″)
C. Hooks bought or made from stiff wire and shaped as illustrated

Instructions
1. Fold cloth B and sew to make 4 bags.
2. Shape and hem canvas A to make belt.
3. Sew bags to canvas belt A.
4. Bend wire to make hooks C.
5. Sew hooks C to canvas belt A.
6. Sew tapes or string to canvas belt A.

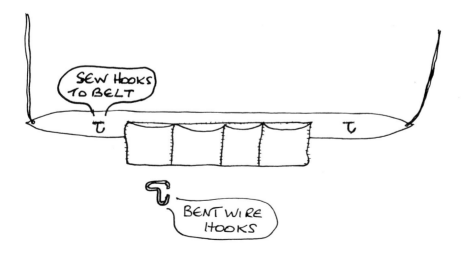